MW00617386

Island Naturalist

by

Kathie Fiveash

Reissued with a revised cover — June 2015
Book © Penobscot Bay Press, Inc., 2014, 2015
All rights reserved.
No part of this book may be reproduced without written permission, except for
brief quotations for review purposes.

ISBN: 978-0-941238-18-2
Library of Congress Control Number: 2014942229

Editor Caroline Spear
Copy Editor James Straub
Cover Designer George Eaton
Book Designers George Eaton and Jeremiah Savage
Paginator George Eaton

Cover photograph of Gray Seal by Marnie Davis.
Back cover photo of tree by John DeWitt.

Published by Penobscot Books,
a division of Penobscot Bay Press Community Information Services
P.O. Box 36, 69 Main Street, Stonington ME 04681 USA
Tel: 207-367-2200
Fax: 207-367-6397
Email: books@pbp.me
Web: penbaypress.me
Printed in the USA by 360 Digital Books
Kalamazoo, Michigan USA

For my grandchildren, Jack and Leo

Acknowledgements

My deepest thanks go to my partner, Albert Gordon, whose inquiring mind, excellent editing skills, attention to detail, love for the island, and steadfast faith in me made this book possible.

Many thanks to my island naturalist friends John DeWitt and Marnie Davis, and to my cousin Joan Handel, who generously contributed their beautiful photographs, almost all taken on Isle au Haut, to this book. Thanks also to Robert Abuza, who shared his picture of the monarch butterfly caterpillar in the milkweed by my front door.

Thank you to Roger Hooke, geology guru par excellence, who patiently guided me through many revisions of the article on the geology of Isle au Haut. I learned so much from you, Roger!

Thank you to all the excellent Isle au Haut naturalists and fishermen, especially Greg Runge and Billy Barter, who have wisely and patiently helped me more than they know to understand nature on the island.

Last but not least, thanks to you, my readers, for being out there and being interested.

It's all I have to bring today—
This, and my heart beside—
This, and my heart, and all the fields—
And all the meadows wide—
Be sure you count—should I forget
Some one the sum could tell—
This, and my heart, and all the Bees
Which in the Clover dwell.

Emily Dickinson

Contents

Fall 133

Winter

Introduction

This book is one of the fruits of a lifetime of interest in the natural world. From the time I was a small child, I have always paid attention outdoors. To look, listen, smell, touch and taste in nature has been my delight and pastime since childhood. I prefer to be out alone or with my dog, toting binoculars and field guides, free to stop wherever and whenever I want, with no one else impatiently urging me to get a move on. I enjoy reverie. I like to lose track of time. But as I get older, I am more soberly aware of the reckless actions of humans, which imperil the earth and all its beings. I feel it is increasingly important that we humans understand our connections to the multitudes of living beings that share the earth with us. Writing about nature is one way for me to encourage environmental awareness and maybe even activism. It is my hope that this book will help you, my readers, to go outdoors with your minds and senses alert, and to experience the coast of Maine for yourselves.

If we move through life with earbuds in our ears and screens in front of our faces, we will surely miss the details of flowers, trees, birds, insects, and clouds. When I walk on streets, shop in stores, wait in airports, or even sit around with friends in living rooms, I am troubled at the number of people who are giving their attention to things or people that aren't really there. People are talking on cell phones, listening to iPods, consulting computers and iPads, watching television, tweeting, texting, posting on Facebook, and playing video games. The real world of the present time and place seems at times to have receded from the forefront of our consciousness.

On the other hand, if we study the natural environment where we live, we come closer to understanding the huge web of life that holds us in place. If we walk through the real world paying attention, if we give weight and value to local plants and animals, to the sky and the water and the rocks around us, our home is sure to become more interesting and more beautiful. What does it really mean to call a place home? Here is the story of how I came to be at home on a Maine island.

Fifteen years ago, I moved to Isle au Haut to join my old friend and new partner Albert, and to make a new life for myself. It was a big change. I had lived all my adult life in Cambridge, Massachusetts. I was part of a human community linked by ties of family, lifelong friendships, and shared interests. I had worked for twenty years as a classroom teacher in urban schools that served hundreds of children, and where my own children were educated. I had spent my free time exploring the mountains, woods, fields, ponds, lakes, and rivers of New England. I enjoyed a deep-seated sense of having both a human and a natural home.

Then, after my marriage of twenty-five years ended and both my children were in college, I was given the gift of a sabbatical year. I began a master's degree program in Environmental Studies at Antioch New England in Keene, New Hampshire. To do this I moved for the year to a one-room octagonal cabin in the woods of southern New Hampshire. My cabin was a third of a mile down a track through the woods from the farm where my landlord lived. I had to leave my car at the farm and walk in. The cabin had electricity and a wood stove, but no plumbing. It stood in a grassy clearing in the woods near the Ashuelot River, surrounded by big white pines. It was the first and only place I have ever lived that was entirely my own.

I moved in during the early summer. I spent the days studying and writing, walking in the woods, identifying birds and flowers and trees. I often went to watch my nearest neighbors, the beavers, emerge from their lodge as darkness fell. In the night I listened to barred owls calling in the woods around me and saw the brightness of the stars without ambient light. I was often lonely and restless, but I was also entranced by the simplicity and beauty of my little world.

In the fall, my landlord dumped piles of firewood in the middle of the clearing, driving a rickety old tractor that pulled an overloaded trailer creaking and swaying down the hill. I stacked wood. My arms got strong. All winter I hiked in and out on snowshoes, hauling everything I needed—water, groceries, laundry, books—in a little red plastic sled down to my cabin. I heated the water for my one-gallon daily shower on the woodstove, poured it into a plastic sunshower bag that hung from a beam in the cabin, and washed standing in a pretty blue plastic washtub. I reused that precious water for dishwashing, and once again for watering my plants. Then the springtime came.

I will never forget that spring. It came like a wave, washing over everything around me, quiet, subtle, transformative. In Cambridge the spring is always colorful with the hundreds of spectacularly blooming cultivars that people plant in their yards and gardens—crocuses, azaleas, crabapples, cherries, daffodils, tulips. These cultivated plants somehow overshadow the natural spring going on around them. But in my clearing the unadorned spring was more beautiful to me than spring had ever been before. It needed no help from humans. It came in buds and birdsong, in melt and rain and the flooding river, in sunshine and woodland wildflowers, in the smells of wetness and rot, in wood frogs and peepers. That spring taught me that it was time for me to move out of the city. Then my friend Albert from Isle au Haut came courting, and I decided to give up my city life for the opportunity to live with him on a wild, unbridged, sparsely populated Maine island where I had no family, no friends, and no work. If that sounds crazy, it probably was.

But really, it wasn't crazy! It was just the beginning of a long process of learning to call Isle au Haut home. I'm thankful that I now belong to a human community of fishermen, builders, teachers, cooks, jacks-of-all-trades, entrepreneurs, in-betweeners, and summer folks. I have voted at Town Meetings, joined committees, and made close friendships. I have taught Music and Island Ecology in the one-room K-8 public school with anywhere from four to twelve students enrolled. I've become a serious gardener, fished for lobsters, raised chickens for eggs and meat, filled freezers with home-grown food, learned to can pickles, jams, and jellies. And most important, I've studied the natural history of the island.

I had never before lived by the ocean or in a spruce forest or among bogs and granite and sphagnum moss. I was far from my familiar natural world. For a natural-ist like me, it was like moving to a foreign country. Home had always been the place where I knew the land, the trees, the flowers, the animals and birds and insects, and where I had a sense of how they are all connected to each other. To make Isle au Haut my home I needed to know it in that way. I had the time and the inclination to explore the nature of Isle au Haut, its rocky shores, its spruce forests, its bogs, its meadows, its clam flats, its ponds, its streams, and its marshes. Looking east from our house I watched the tides rise and fall under the influence of the waxing and waning moon. I saw the sunrise move slowly north and south along the horizon as the seasons turned. I learned about sea birds, eagles, seals, deer, lobsters, tide pools, seaweed, and a thousand other details of island life. I asked questions of the good naturalists who have lived here a long time. I taught ecology in the school, crowding the whole student body into the back of our pickup truck to explore all the different island habitats. What a great way to learn!

In the late spring of 2010, I asked Nat Barrows, the editor of the Stonington, Maine, newspaper *Island Ad-Vantages*, if he would be interested in a natural history column. We came to an agreement, and I began writing. This book is a compilation of the columns I have written since then. It is arranged, as it was written, by season. I hope the book will be a reference that will help you to explore your own connections to this wild, beautiful, and unique place that is the coast of Maine.

Isle au Haut in Geologic Time

Sometimes when I walk the shores and high places of Isle au Haut I ponder the history of the rocks. They seem so permanent. I think about the recent history of the land, how the island was once almost totally cleared for sheep farming. Stone walls, now deep in the forest, served as sheep fences in pastures. Gnarled apple trees mark the sites of long-ago homesteads now overshadowed by fast growing spruce. Throughout human history on the island only the rocks have endured, apparently little changed by the vagaries of time.

Geologic time dwarfs time as we humans experience it. The earth is 4.5 billion years old. Our species has been walking the earth for about 200,000 years. We have been here for less than 0.005% of the earth's history. It is difficult and humbling to research geologic time and to imagine its vastness and the huge changes that have transformed our landscape. But I know that understanding geologic time is essential to my understanding both of the place where I live and of what it means to be a human being.

The rocks that form Isle au Haut and much of midcoast Maine are young as rocks go. They were born about 425 million years ago in volcanic eruptions under an ancient ocean geologists call Iapetus. At that time, an arc of these volcanic islands called Avalonia, rather like present-day Japan, was moving westward towards what is now North America. These islands eventually became our area of the coast of Maine. Roughly 380 million years ago the leading edge of Avalonia crashed, in titanic slow motion, into Laurentia, a supercontinent that included North America. The rocks that are now inland Maine were a part of that supercontinent.

Then, 300 million years ago, the supercontinent called Gondwana, which included the continental plates that are now Europe, Asia, Africa, Australia, and India, crashed into Laurentia, and the Iapetus Ocean closed. The volcanic island chains that are now the rocks of coastal Maine were crushed between the two colliding plates. This collision of Gondwana and Laurentia created a larger supercontinent geologists call Pangaea. What is now Maine was situated in the middle of Pangaea, far from any ocean, near the latitude and longitude where Ghana is today. In the equatorial warmth, life proliferated. About 225 million years ago, dinosaurs evolved and began to diversify on Pangaea.

After 25 million more years, Pangaea began to break apart close to the suture lines between the merged continental plates. Magma rose up from beneath the earth's crust, breaking the plates apart and creating three new supercontinents, one consisting of what is now North America, one including Europe and Asia, and the third containing South America and Africa. Remember the rocks in the volcanic island chains that were formed by eruptions beneath the Iapetus Ocean 225 million years earlier? The volcanic islands that were crushed between the colliding continents? The rocks from those old volcanic islands stuck to the edge of the North American plate as North America broke apart from Europe. They are the rocks that are now our part of the coast of Maine. The North Atlantic Ocean, which is still getting wider today, was born.

Fifty million years later, about 150 million years ago, another rift caused by upwelling magma split Africa from South America and opened the South Atlantic Ocean. Throughout the time since the breakup of Pangaea, the North American continental plate, which includes the land that is now Maine, has been traveling north and west, slowly rotating clockwise over the underlying mantle. We are still moving west today.

Over the past 50 million years the earth's climate has cooled. About three million years ago, cooling accelerated and the arctic ice cap formed and grew. In the past 800,000 years there have been at least eight major glaciations of the northern hemisphere. The last of these glacial periods happened during the past 110,000 years, when human life was already evolving. This period, called the Wisconsinan by geologists, included several substages during which the ice advanced, retreated, and then advanced again. The ice sheet that glaciated North America during the Wisconsinan period is called the Laurentide Ice Sheet. With each new advance, the ice sheet wiped the land mostly clean of the effects of the previous advance. Nomadic Ice Age people moved south before the oncoming edge of the ice sheet, then moved north again as the ice retreated, hunting the mammoths, mastodons and other large mammals that proliferated at that time.

At the peak of its most recent advance southward, roughly 22,000 years ago, ice was two miles thick in northern Canada and slightly over a mile thick over Isle au Haut. This final southward journey of the ice sheet was responsible for extensively modifying the features that now distinguish the Maine coast. The ice was incredibly heavy, laced with rocks and sand. As the glacier moved south it gouged north-south features such as Isle au Haut's Long Pond. It scratched and polished the surface rock. It scraped the soil out of valleys, exposing bedrock. It shaped mountains as it moved southward, forming long, smooth slopes on the northern flanks and plucking rock off the southern edges, creating steep contours. As the glacier started to melt away 22,000 years ago it left huge piles of rubble called glacial moraines, like New York's Long Island, at its southern extremity. It deposited masses of rocks, gravel, and sand, and left large boulders called glacial erratics strewn along the path of its retreat.

The glacier not only extensively modified the landscape, it also weighed so much that it depressed the crust of the earth beneath it. There is a complex history of sea level change on the Maine coast. When great quantities of ocean water were frozen into the glaciers, sea level worldwide went down. However, the weight of the ice depressed the crust of the earth underneath it, so that Maine's coastal areas were below sea level.

As the ice retreated, the land began to rebound, and sea levels rose. About 14,000 years ago, the sea level in coastal Maine was 230 feet higher than today. The Atlantic Ocean lapped on shores near Millinocket. By 11,000 years ago the land, released from the weight of the ice, had rebounded to such an extent that sea level on the coast of Maine fell to 180 feet below the present level. The coastline moved hundreds of yards offshore. Isle au Haut was at that time connected to the mainland by land bridges created in shallow areas when sea level fell. Eventually sea level rose again, the land and the sea reached their current configuration, and the islands and bays we know today came to be.

The geography of the coast of Maine and the islands continues to change, but so slowly that careful scientific measurements are needed to detect the changes. We have developed instruments sensitive enough to record change that is so slight we cannot see it, but we have not developed an informed understanding of where we fit in the great march of earth's history. Humans have only walked the earth for an eyeblink of geologic time, yet we think of ourselves as having a long history. Humans began settling in cities and building what Western people call civilization less than 10,000 years ago. Dinosaurs endured on earth for 160 million years. I wonder how well adapted our brand new species will prove to be in the long run. Looking at the current state of the planet, I'm not sure Homo sapiens will stand the test of geologic time.

Spring

Sap

When I was a teenager in Vermont, I used to ski into the woods during sugaring season in late February and early March. I would bring along a small metal cup. I loved drinking sap out of the buckets hanging on sugar maples tapped by local farmers. When I came to a stand of tapped maples I would stop, remove the cover from a bucket, and dip a cupful of sap. It was the most refreshing of drinks. It tasted like ice-cold water with the slightest hint of sweetness. I felt that I was imbibing the essence of spring.

Sap starts running in maple trees when the nights are below freezing and the days warm up into the forties. On a really good day a harvester can extract as much as three gallons of sap from a single tree. The average amount of sap gathered from one tree in the sugaring season is about 13 gallons. The sap that is gathered for maple syrup is less than a tenth of the total sap produced by the tree. That means that every day during the sap run, half a ton of sap is flowing up and down the tree. How can a maple tree lift this amazing weight and volume of sap every day?

The answer to this question is that in maple trees, unlike almost all other trees, the xylem, as we call the vessels that conduct sap upwards, is surrounded by cells and intracellular spaces that are filled with air rather than liquid. On cold nights when the tree starts to freeze, water diffuses through the walls of the xylem, condenses inside these air-filled spaces, and then freezes. This process pulls more water up the xylem from the roots, and is the driving force behind the rising of sap in the tree. This sap replaces the water that has diffused into the air-filled spaces. The rising sap carries dissolved sugars, which have been stored in the roots all winter. The colder the night, the more sap is pulled up as the tree freezes. Then, when the temperature warms during the day, the extra sap accumulated in the air spaces as the ice melts diffuses back into the xylem and is pulled by gravity down the tree. So really, the sap flows up the tree as it freezes at night and down the tree as it melts in the daytime. Sugar harvesters extract this down-flowing sap, and the end result for us, after a lot of boiling to concentrate the sugars, is maple syrup.

All trees have sap, but most of them do not have an early spring sap flow like maples. In most trees the xylem tubes carrying sap up the tree are not surrounded by spaces filled with air, but by spaces filled with water. The sap in the xylem simply freezes and thaws, but does not move. In late spring, after the leaves unfold and begin to photosynthesize, sap flows up the tree from the roots to replace the water that is evaporating out of the leaves during photosynthesis. During the growing season, this is how sap moves up in all trees including maples. Sap moving up a tree to supply the leaves contains mostly water and minerals absorbed out of the soil by the roots.

There is another kind of sap that moves around in trees during the growing season. This sap transports the sugar produced by photosynthesis in the leaves to wherever it is needed. The system of vessels that transports this energy-rich sap in a tree is called phloem. Unlike the xylem, which only carries sap upwards from the roots (except in maples in the early spring), the phloem moves sap from parts of the tree with high concentrations of sugar to parts of the tree with low concentrations of sugar. When new leaves and flowers emerge, stored sugars are moved up from the roots to provide energy for new growth. Once the tree has leafed out and is photosynthesizing, the sugar produced in the leaves is moved into the rest of the tree.

Most of a tree is wood, a non-living tissue, created each year right beneath the bark by the cambium, a thin layer of cells where new phloem and the xylem are generated. This is how annual growth rings are formed. When wood is first created, it is part of the xylem, and conducts sap up the tree. But each year, new xylem is formed. The old xylem dies and becomes the hard, fibrous, strong material that supports the tree and allows it to stand tall. As we watch the trees go green in the springtime, it is good to remember that the wood we use for building everything from log cabins to fine furniture once carried sap, the tree's water of life.

American Woodcocks
(Scolopax minor)

I will never forget the first time I witnessed the courtship display of the American woodcock. It was early spring, and I was walking at dusk in a moist field with shrubby edges when I heard a strange, nasal beeping sound. I moved slowly towards it, trying to determine the source. Suddenly, a dark bird exploded out of the grass maybe twenty yards away and flew straight upward in widening spirals. As it rose through the air, it made a twittering sound that faded as the bird ascended to a great height. When it reached the peak of its flight, almost out of sight in the dim light, it began a diving descent, zigzagging downwards while trilling a series of musical chirps, then fell silent near the ground, landed right where it had begun, and began beeping again. The contrast between that cartoonish "peent," as I later learned it is called, and the ecstatic aerial dance was comical and somehow touching. The display went on, over and over, continuing as I left the field in the darkness.

Photo by John DeWitt

Though classified as a shorebird, the woodcock is an upland bird. It prefers wet thickets, moist woods, brushy swamps, and abandoned farmland that is reverting to forest. It is plump and short-legged, about the weight of a robin, with a large round head, a long bill, and big eyes placed high in the head. The placement of its eyes gives the woodcock the ability to see 360 degrees around it, and the entire sky above, one of the largest visual fields of any bird. Thus, a woodcock can easily see predators while feeding or resting. It is well camouflaged, with plumage of mottled brown, rust, gray, and black above, and tan underneath.

Woodcocks winter on the Gulf coast and the southeastern Atlantic states. They migrate north in February, arrive in Maine in March, and immediately begin their breeding season. Males establish individual singing grounds in fields near brushy cover and perform their beautiful courtship flights at dusk and dawn—or all night, if there is bright moonlight. They do a little rumba dance while "peenting" on the ground and then take to the sky. The twittering we hear while the male spirals upward is actually the sound of air rushing through the flight feathers. The chirping on descent is his song. The male's displays attract females out of the underbrush. One male may mate with several females. The female builds her shallow nest on the ground, and raises three or four downy chicks without the male's help. The chicks mature quickly, and are independent by five weeks old.

Woodcocks eat mostly earthworms, grubs, and other invertebrates. They forage by probing soft soil in thickets and swamps where they can remain well hidden while hunting. Their long bills have many sensitive nerve endings and a flexible upper mandible, which gives the woodcock the unique ability to open and close its bill at the tip while the bill is sunk in the earth. This, along with a rough tongue and bill lining, helps the woodcock to feel in the earth and grasp its slippery prey.

On Isle au Haut, woodcocks begin to display in mid-March and will keep on displaying through April. With a little knowledge and a little luck, you may find one at dusk in an open area near your house. Listen carefully as darkness is falling. If you hear a woodcock, you can move closer to it each time it launches into the sky. You will be treated to a unique and beautiful ritual performed by a creature that is usually a recluse, but at this one time of year becomes a prima donna of the bird world.

Red-winged Blackbirds
(Aegelius phoneceus)

For me, the male red-winged blackbird is the premier harbinger of spring. He arrives before the ice is off the lakes, before the snow is melted, before the salamanders and wood frogs breed, before the long, honking vees of Canada geese pass over going north. Male red-winged blackbirds arrive in flocks, and they sing their hearts out over the marshes. It is rare to see only one blackbird. In any cattail marsh there may be dozens or hundreds, each one swaying atop a tattered cattail, periodically declaring his presence by hunching his shoulders, displaying his brilliant scarlet epaulets, and belting out his loud "conk-a-reee" trill. After a winter of chickadee calls and the harsh cries of crows and blue jays, it is a thrilling sound.

Red-winged blackbirds are in the same family as orioles, meadowlarks, bobolinks, and grackles. Red-winged blackbirds exemplify an adaptation called sexual dimorphism, which means that males and females look different from each other. In blackbirds the female is cryptically colored to be inconspicuous on the nest, while the colorful male uses his bright plumage for display in courtship and territorial behaviors. Many familiar birds, including mallard ducks, cardinals, and all the warblers are sexually dimorphic. Red-winged blackbirds range throughout most of North America from Mexico to northern Canada. Though they breed throughout their range, many migrate northwards in the spring. The first flocks to arrive in Maine are actually passing through on their way to Canada.

In late March male redwings arrive in Maine to establish breeding territories, usually in freshwater marshes but sometimes in old fields, wet meadows, or along rivers and streams. Red-winged blackbirds prefer to nest in loose colonies where each male controls a territory within a larger area. The streaky brown females, which outnumber the males by two or three to one, come a few weeks later to choose mates. You would think, given their abundance, that we would see many female redwings, but the females tend to be more secretive than the males, skulking among the reeds, grasses, and bushes to find food and nesting material. Typically, a male will have several females nesting in his territory. Some may have as many as fifteen. But many nestlings hatched inside his territory will not be his offspring because the females often mate with males from adjoining territories as well as with him. Neither partner is monogamous.

Male redwings are aggressively territorial. They spend a lot of time during the breeding season defending territory. Meanwhile, each female chooses a nest site, which is usually low and well hidden in vertical shoots of marsh plants, often above water. The nest is intricately woven of cattail leaves, bark strips, and other vegetation, and lined with mud, leaves, mosses and grasses to make a deep, soft cup. A female redwing may raise as many as three broods during a single summer. For each brood, she constructs a new nest. This prevents nests from becoming infested with parasites that could kill baby birds.

A female redwing lays three to five eggs and incubates them for eleven or twelve days. The nestlings hatch naked and blind, but grow quickly, and by two weeks old are ready to fledge. Females do most of the work of raising the young, which is not surprising since the male may have two to five or more nests to protect. The female forages in the vegetation, feeding her babies insects, spiders, worms, snails, frog eggs, seeds and fruits—whatever she can find that is nutritious. Red-winged blackbirds are enthusiastically omnivorous.

Many animals, including raccoons, minks, snakes, herons, and other birds, prey on the eggs and young of red-winged blackbirds. Marsh wrens, which compete with redwings for nesting territory and food, often puncture and eat redwing eggs—and the redwings will return the favor. The better concealed the nest, the more likely it is to avoid predation. The colonial nesting strategy of redwings helps with this problem, because many alert adults are keeping watch in any nesting area. Male redwings act as sentinels and are aggressive and fearless. They will attack much larger predators, often calling for help from other males and mobbing the intruder—even a creature as large as a human.

In the early fall, our red-winged blackbirds gather in huge mixed flocks to migrate south with grackles, starlings, and cowbirds. New England birds, and birds from other northern areas, are migratory and head for the mid-Atlantic and southern states to spend the winter. Blackbirds from the western and central states are mostly non-migratory. During fall migration, as in the spring, males precede females. The sexes never migrate together. When they are in their winter flocks, red-winged black-birds change their diet, relying primarily on foraging in open fields and agricultural areas for seeds and grains. A flock can number in the millions of birds, which roost together at night. They spread out in a fifty mile radius to feed in the daytime, and return to their roost again as night falls.

In March the spring migration is beginning. Despite raw temperatures and bleak landscapes, birds are heading north to breed in the country of long daylight, abundant insect life, and open nesting territory. Some, like the red-winged blackbirds, come so early that they push the edges of spring's envelope, braving snowfall, cold temperatures and scant food supplies. But red-winged blackbirds are among the most abundant North American birds, and their predictable arrival in early spring raises the expectations and the spirits of all the birdwatchers like me who are welcoming them back.

Spotted Salamanders
(Ambystoma maculatum)

Every year in late March or early April a remarkable event takes place. The first rainy night with temperatures in the mid-forties or above is the signal for spotted salamanders to come out of their burrows and hiding places in the forest, make their way to vernal pools, and perform their extraordinary mating ritual.

You may never have seen a spotted salamander, though they are common in our northeastern forests. Spotted salamanders are six to nine inches long, black with irregular rows of bright yellow spots from head to tail. They live as long as twenty years. They spend their lives below ground in deserted rodent burrows, in deep leaf litter, or under stones and logs. They eat earthworms, slugs, snails, insects and insect larvae—whatever they can find in their underground haunts. They are solitary and secretive. Spotted salamanders overwinter deep in the earth below the frost line, remaining inactive until temperatures rise above freezing in the early spring.

Then comes that first warm wet night. Spotted salamanders emerge from their hiding places en masse and migrate through the darkness towards the vernal pools where they began their lives. Vernal pools are crucial to the lives of many woodland amphibians because they hold water from early spring through early summer, but dry out before autumn. Therefore they do not support fish that would prey on amphibian eggs. Each salamander returns to the vernal pool where it hatched. Hundreds or thousands of salamanders may converge on a single vernal pool on the same night. Males outnumber females by more than two to one, sometimes ten to one.

Once they reach their natal pool, salamanders begin their mating ritual, which is carried out in total darkness. They must use chemical clues, probably pheromones, to find and interact with each other. The males gather in groups called congresses, which may have as many as 200 individuals. They wriggle around, rubbing against each other in a courtship dance. They become more aroused as females enter the water. Each excited male deposits small white packets of sperm called spermatophores on the leaf litter at the bottom of the pool. Each male continues to dance, nudging and swimming around a female, trying to attract her to his sperm packets. Each female scoops up spermatophores with her cloaca, an opening in her abdomen. She uses the spermatophores to fertilize her eggs internally.

Within hours, or sometimes a couple of days, each female lays one or more masses of about 100 eggs, attaching them to twigs or underwater vegetation. Each dark, round egg is contained in a clear, gelatinous globe, and the whole mass is held together in a jelly-like orb that absorbs water and swells to about the size of a tennis ball. Many females attach their egg masses to the same branch or clump of vegetation. In the daylight you can see numerous egg masses grouped together in one area of the pool. Within a day or two of their arrival, all the adult salamanders disperse back to the forest until the next spring, leaving their eggs to develop in the pool.

The eggs hatch after one or two months, depending on water temperature. The larvae are slender, about one half inch long, with feathery-looking external gills. Unlike tadpoles, they are carnivorous and prey fiercely on tiny animals in the water and in the leaf litter at the bottom of the pool. As they develop, the larvae grow limbs and lose their external gills. This process is a race against time, because the larval salamanders must mature before the pool dries up. When they leave the pool, they are more than two inches long and are beginning to get their yellow spots. They will not return to the pool until they are sexually mature, two to five years later.

If you are willing to slog out in the dark to a vernal pool on the first warm, rainy night in early spring with a flashlight and high rubber boots, you may get a chance to observe the mating dance of the spotted salamander. You must be careful where you step as you approach the pool, because many salamanders are on the march through the wet woods. Search along the water's edge with your flashlight. When you find a congress of these graceful animals swarming in the dark water, wriggling to the surface every so often to gulp air, descending again into the throng, it is hard to believe that they spend the rest of their lives alone, underground, squeezed into small spaces. Watching them, you feel the excitement of movement, of procreation....of spring.

$\mathcal{S}$kunk $\mathcal{C}$abbage

(Symplocarpus foetidus)

One of the first signs of spring on the island is the emergence of the flowers of skunk cabbage. This remarkable plant is a native perennial that prefers wetlands, stream edges, and boggy woodlands, and it is abundant on Isle au Haut. The flower is encased in a specialized budlike leaf called a spathe. The spathe is about five inches tall and looks like a pointed hood that might be worn by a woodland elf. It is deep purple or maroon, mottled with streaks of yellowish green. Inside the spathe is a composite flower called a spadix, which consists of a knob-like cluster of tightly packed individual flowers without petals. You can see the spadix by peeking into the narrow opening in the spathe: The flower looks like a tiny orange stained purple and studded with white cloves.

Photo by Kathie Fiveash

The skunk cabbage flower is extraordinary because it can generate its own heat. While the spathe is still underground, the developing flower raises the temperature inside the spathe to 30 degrees warmer than the temperature outside. This warmth protects the flower from freezing and radiates outwards, thawing the soil and allowing the spathe to push upwards to the surface. It is during this heating period of about two weeks that the flower emerges, blooms, and releases the skunky odor that gives the plant its name.

Carrion flies, which hatch in early spring and look for rotting flesh in which to lay their eggs, are attracted by the smell of skunk cabbage. They crawl over the spadix, inadvertently pollinating it as they enjoy the cozy interior of the spathe. The first beetles and spiders also congregate there, drawn by the warmth. Once I found a little spider web spun over the opening in a spathe. I'm sure the enterprising spider got a good meal trapping the creatures drawn by the odor and the warmth of the skunk cabbage flower.

Side by side with the spathe, but growing from a separate stem, is the large, pointed leafbud. This bud contains all the leaves of the skunk cabbage plant, each wrapped around the next. When the flower and the spathe start to wilt, the leaves begin their rapid unfurling. The bud pushes upward and the leaves unfold one after the other from the outside in. Each leaf is fleshy and egg-shaped with a large central stalk, and can grow to be three feet long. The mature, fountain-shaped plant is bushy and may be four feet across. The leaves, if broken, give off the same sulfurous smell as the flowers. The wet, early summer woods on the island are studded with big, bright-green skunk cabbage plants.

By mid summer, skunk cabbage begins to die back. The skunk cabbage plant, from spathe and spadix to leaves, is spongy, and lacks fibrous tissues. When it dies back, it doesn't dry out like most plants. It decays, becoming slimy and then dissolving rapidly, leaving behind only its pea-sized red seeds. By late August, this plant that dominated the wetlands in the spring has disappeared from view.

But the roots of the skunk cabbage are still at work. Skunk cabbage has a thick underground stem called a rootstock, which sprouts a huge root system with no taproot. The horizontally wrinkled roots contract after growing downwards, pulling the root-stock deeper into the earth each year. A mature plant may be decades old.

Skunk cabbage has a bad reputation because of its smell. But its unusual flower has a strange beauty, coming before other plants awaken. And children relish breaking a leaf and exclaiming over the foul odor, which quickly dissipates in the open air. Skunk cabbage is our largest woodland wildflower. It is perfectly suited to its swampy habitats. Though its name and smell may be unappealing, skunk cabbage is a plant with amazing adaptations and unique beauty.

Mud Season

In Maine we call it the fifth season. This is the time of year when unpaved roads can become a mud and gravel soup. Sometimes no matter how intrepid your vehicle may be in every other road condition, you will have to get out and walk. And you had better have your boots on.

Mud season happens because the ground thaws from the top down. The frost line, which is the depth to which groundwater in soil freezes in winter, can be as deep as four feet in coastal Maine. Water can't drain from the surface through the underlying layer of ice. As temperatures rise in early spring, snowmelt, along with spring rain, has nowhere to go. As the thaw progresses, first we get puddles, then we get mud, then deeper mud. If it gets deeper than your vehicle's clearance, you had better not drive. At last, the thaw is complete, the water drains away, and the mud miraculously disappears, sometimes so quickly that if you were to run errands in the morning through practically impassible mud ruts, you could return only a few hours later to your familiar old road.

Some mud seasons are much worse than others, and it is hard to predict each year how muddy the mud will be. The colder and longer the winter, the deeper the frost line. The deeper the frost line, the farther warmth needs to penetrate into the soil before that water can drain away. The depth of the snowpack matters, too. The more snow, the more water is trapped in the mud. Since roads are usually plowed, the insulating effect of the snow, which protects woods and fields from the deepest frost, doesn't help on our dirt roads. They are exposed all winter to the most severe temperatures.

The type of soil also affects mud season. Sandy soil drains much faster than soil with a high clay content. There is also the question of the early spring rains. Lots of rain makes lots of mud. And the faster our temperatures warm up in the spring, the faster the ground will thaw. There are so many factors affecting the severity and length of mud season—depth of frost, snow pack and spring rain, type of soil, spring temperatures—that it is difficult to predict how long drivers will be cursing the mud and waiting for the thaw.

We are not the only creatures who wait for the end of mud season. Isle au Haut's four species of snake—garter snakes, ring-necked snakes, green snakes, and red-bellied snakes—hibernate in communal dens, called hibernacula, below the frost line. Hundreds of snakes, sometimes snakes of different species, gather each fall in these traditional dens deep underground to wait for the end of the ice. Garter snakes in particular are famous for traveling up to two miles to join huge aggregations of other snakes in a hibernaculum where they stay all winter. Once the ground thaws in spring they emerge slowly, at first only in the daytime, returning to the hibernaculum during the colder nights. Garter snakes breed in the spring right after they emerge—this makes it easy for them to find mates before they disperse for the summer months.

Earthworms also wait out winter below the frost line in little tangled balls. Just as water can't move down through the soil until the frost is gone, earthworms can't move up. I always know that the ground has thawed when I come out one spring morning and there are worm castings, those little squiggles of soil excreted by earthworms, decorating the lawn. Each year, when the gentle earthworm returns to the surface to begin another season of tirelessly working the soil, my heart lifts. Worm castings are a sure sign of spring.

$\mathcal{S}$pring Peepers

(Pseudacris crucifer)

Once, a few years ago, on a warm, wet night in early April, I ventured into a hummocky wetland full of spring peepers. As I approached, the pleasant, sleigh bell-like sound grew louder and louder. Wearing tall rubber boots and carrying a flashlight, I stepped carefully from hummock to hummock into the swamp until I was well inside. At first, the nearby peepers fell silent, but as I stood quietly in the darkness, all resumed their chorus. I soon felt as if I were standing in the middle of a room full of smoke detectors going off—the shrill, piercing calls of the tiny frogs made an almost unbearable cacophony around me. I tried to locate individual frogs, shining my flashlight at spots where I thought the calls originated, but despite what seemed like thousands of frog voices all around me, I was not able to see a single one.

Spring peepers are tiny frogs, each about an inch long, tan or brown with a characteristic dark "X" scrawled on their backs. They live in forests, wetlands, and meadows throughout eastern and midwestern North America. They are New England's smallest, loudest, and possibly most abundant frog species. Despite their prevalence, they are difficult to see. Peepers are nocturnal and extremely well camouflaged. They sit perfectly still when approached. The best way to find one is to go looking with one or two friends during the spring chorus. If you stand three or four feet apart and all aim your flashlights at the place you think you hear a particular frog, you are likely to find it close to where the beams intersect.

Peepers spend the winter in hibernation in the leaf litter, under stones, or behind loose tree bark. They are able to withstand freezing because their bodies produce glucose prior to hibernation. This natural antifreeze protects their cells from rupturing at sub-freezing temperatures. Peepers awaken and emerge from their winter beds in early spring during the first rains. They migrate at night to nearby vernal pools and other semi-permanent wetlands for their spring mating rituals. Peepers, like many woodland amphibians, prefer to breed in pools where fish are absent, but where there is enough water to last during the three-month development of their tadpoles.

Once peepers have gathered at a wetland, the males establish tiny territories, often less than a square foot, and begin to sing. They call from grassy mounds, low vegetation or the water's edge. When a male peeper calls, he inflates his throat into a tight balloon and flexes his tiny body over and over, forcing out a series of loud peeps. On a warm wet night in April he calls at least once a second all night long.

A female chooses her mate based on his size and the speed of his vocalizations. Once she has chosen a mate she allows him to clasp her from behind beneath her forelimbs, and they swim off together in a prolonged embrace called amplexus. The male will not let go. (I recently stopped my car to rescue a frog off the road and found it was actually two frogs in amplexus who did not separate despite being picked up and carried to the roadside.) The frog pair dives together to the bottom of the pool and the female lays about 900 eggs, depositing them singly or in small clumps under the leaf litter, on fallen branches, and on underwater plants. The male fertilizes the eggs externally as they are laid. After exhausting her egg supply, the female leaves the breeding pool while the male returns to his territory to resume the business of attracting females. By mid-May the nightly chorus is dying off, and the breeding is finished. The adult frogs disperse, leaving their eggs behind.

The eggs hatch in about a week depending on water temperature. The tiny tadpoles, less than ½ inch long, are abundant prey for many small predators—diving beetles, leeches, dragonfly nymphs, large spiders, giant water bugs, newts, and other frogs. One of the peeper tadpole's defense mechanisms is inactivity, which makes it difficult to see, but also slows its feeding and its growth. It takes a peeper tadpole from 85 to 100 days to mature into a frog, which in Maine would be late July or early August. The tadpole is initially legless and herbivorous. It breathes with gills. As it feeds on algae, it gets bigger and grows hindlimbs, then forelimbs, and finally absorbs its tadpole tail into its frog body. In this last phase of development, the tadpole loses its gills, becoming an air breather with lungs, though, like all frogs, it can also breathe through its wet skin when inactive. During this phase the little peeper refashions its digestive system and becomes a carnivore, ready to venture into the woods and fields to hunt.

Adult peepers are nocturnal. They prey on a variety of small invertebrates like spiders, sowbugs, leafhoppers, ants, caterpillars and ticks. Despite the fact that they have toe pads on their feet that make them good climbers, peepers prefer to stay in low vegetation or on the forest floor. Little is known about their lives outside their breeding pools—they are difficult to study because they are difficult to find. By being active at night, peepers avoid predation by most birds, but are hunted by owls, snakes, salamanders, large spiders, and shrews. Peepers are slow to reach sexual maturity, and do not breed until they are two or three years old.

The spring peeper is a perfect example of an animal that is around us all the time, whose existence we forget for all but a few short weeks of the year. In late March or early April, the chilly silence of early spring nights is suddenly broken by the clamor of thousands of little creatures intent on reproduction. A large peeper chorus on a wet night can be heard up to half a mile away. It is a spring wake-up call. People phone each other, post on Facebook, bundle up and sit in the dark on their back porches, stop their cars on lonely roads to roll down their windows in the rain, and listen together: "Peepers!"

Brown-headed Cowbirds
(Molothrus ater)

Every spring I am glad to see returning migratory birds at my feeder. All except one—the brown-headed cowbird. The cowbird is a relative of blackbirds, grackles, and orioles, and looks rather like a small blackbird with a short, finch-like bill. The males are a glossy black with brown heads. The females are pale grey-brown. Their looks have nothing to do with my unwelcoming attitude towards them. My objections are based on their reproductive strategy, which is called brood parasitism.

Photo by Joan Handel

Brood parasitism occurs when a female bird lays her eggs in other birds' nests, leaving the other birds to incubate and care for her young. In North America, the brown-headed cowbird is the only common brood parasite. In one season, a single cowbird may lay as many as 40 eggs in 40 different nests. The most common hosts for cowbird eggs are song sparrows, phoebes, goldfinches, and various warblers. But cowbirds, which are native to the entire continental United States, have been recorded as attempting to parasitize more than 200 different species of birds from hummingbirds to hawks. This strategy allows cowbirds to spend their energy on mating, feeding, and producing lots of eggs rather than on incubating and feeding their young.

Cowbirds' parasitizing behavior affects their hosts in many ways. First, when a cowbird lays her egg in another's nest, she often pushes one or more of the host's eggs out. Cowbird eggs, like those of most brood parasites, have short incubation periods. This means that a young cowbird hatches before the rest of the brood. A young cowbird grows especially rapidly, making huge demands on its foster parents for food that might have fed the legitimate nestlings. The baby cowbird is aggressive and is usually larger than its nestmates. It may push its nestmates out of the nest, smother them in the nest, or outright kill them. For many common cowbird hosts, such as song sparrows, more than half of nests in any given area may be parasitized. The success of these nests in producing a new generation of song sparrows is reduced by as much as 50 percent. Experts cite cowbird parasitism, along with pollution, habitat destruction and fragmentation, and domestic cats, as a major cause of population decline in many migratory songbird species.

How do host birds respond to the threat of brood parasitism by cowbirds? There are many answers to this question depending on the species of the host. Probably the best defense is to avoid the cowbird threat altogether by concealing the nest effectively. Colonial nesting is also a good defense: birds that nest in groups, such as purple finches, can repel incoming cowbirds. Some birds, such as phoebes and many warblers, seem not to notice the cowbird's egg, despite the fact that it is larger than their own eggs, and often differently marked and colored. They simply do their best to raise the young cowbird along with their own chicks. Some, like yellow warblers, recognize the intruding egg but are too small to push it out of their nest. Instead, they weave a new nest on top of the old nest in hopes that the cowbird will not return. Researchers have found yellow warbler nests with three or four layers. Some birds abandon the parasitized nest and rebuild. Some larger birds, like robins, blue jays, and catbirds can puncture cowbird eggs or push them from their nests.

Cowbirds, however, often stay in the area where they have laid their eggs and monitor them. If her egg has been ejected or killed, the female cowbird may exhibit what is called "mafia behavior" and destroy the nest of the rebellious foster parents. In many cases it may be preferable for the host birds to knuckle under and raise the baby cowbird in order to assure the survival of at least some of their own chicks.

Before the arrival of Europeans in North America, cowbirds were primarily residents of the central prairies where they followed the buffalo herds, feeding on insects stirred up by the passage of the buffalo. This nomadic lifestyle complemented brood parasitism as a reproductive strategy since a cowbird confined to a nest would be unable to move with the herd. Today, cowbirds are found in many habitats. They prefer the fragmented landscapes created by humans: field and forest edges, agricultural areas, and suburbs. They are omnivores, eating seeds and insects, and are common feeder birds, especially during migration.

Every year, I breathe a sigh of resignation when I see my first cowbird. I know that many of the local nesting birds I love, including song sparrows, common yellowthroats, and goldfinches, may be cowbird victims. And yet, I have to grudgingly admire the success of the cowbird, which uses what seems to humans a dirty trick, but is actually an extremely successful adaptation for survival.

American Robins
(Turdus migratorius)

One of the first birdwatching experiences I can remember is seeing a flock of migrating robins. I was seven years old, on February vacation in Florida with my grandparents. It was early evening, and I looked up to see a huge flock of robins, their orange breasts illuminated by the rays of the setting sun, passing on and on above me heading north. My grandfather told me that soon they would be in New England building their nests and having babies.

The American robin is our most ubiquitous songbird. It is the largest member of the thrush family, a group of plump, brown, woodland songbirds that feed mostly on the ground. It got its name in colonial days from English settlers nostalgic for the robin redbreast, a small, friendly European bird with colors similar to our robin. All over America people see robins hopping and running on lawns and singing cheerfully from high perches. Most of us have found their bulky nests or discovered the broken shells of their blue eggs on the ground. Birdwatchers use robins as a standard: "Is it bigger or smaller than a robin?"

Robins range throughout North America. Most are migratory, moving as far south as southern Mexico in the winter, and as far north as northern Canada in the spring. Some stay on their breeding grounds all year if they are able to find food there. Robins' breeding range includes the entire continental United States except Florida, and most of Canada. As the climate warms, robins' winter range is shifting north into New England.

In the springtime, the arrival of robins corresponds with the awakening of earthworms, their favorite food. As the soil reaches about 36 degrees, earthworms come to the surface, and soon robins are there to gobble them up. So when you look down and see the first worm castings on the ground, look up! You may see the first flocks of migratory robins moving north before they disperse onto their breeding grounds.

Male robins arrive before females. Since robins sing almost exclusively when breeding, you'll know a breeding robin has arrived when you hear the familiar "cheerup, cheerily, cheerio" song, usually given from a prominent perch. The male robin uses his song to establish his territory and attract his mate. An arriving female, lured by his musical prowess, chooses him, and the courtship begins. The female does all the nest building, and she builds three nests every summer to raise three different broods, all with the same husband. She builds each nest by shaping a cup of grasses, rootlets, and bark strips, and then plastering the outside with mud. By building a new, clean nest for each brood, she discourages the growth of parasites that might harm her nestlings. Her first nest, built before the trees leaf out, is often hidden in an evergreen tree. Subsequent nests are usually on horizontal branches amid dense deciduous vegetation. Sometimes a robin builds on a human-made structure such as an eave or outdoor light fixture. The female lays three to five eggs and incubates them for two weeks while the male guards and feeds her.

Young robins hatch helpless and naked, their bulging eyes sealed shut. Newly hatched robins throw back their heads, open their outsized yellow-lined beaks, and chirp loudly when their parents arrive with an earthworm or caterpillar to jam down their throats. As soon as it eats, a baby robin poops. The vigilant parent immediately scoops the poop and throws it over the side to keep the nest clean. Robins hunt constantly to feed their young. Contrary to popular belief, robins hunt by sight—they do not locate worms by listening for them. Thirteen days after hatching, baby robins are feathered out and ready to fledge, or leave the nest.

Both parents continue to feed their young on the ground and in low vegetation for a few days while the fledglings' flying skills improve. Then the father carries on feeding the first brood and taking them to a communal robin roost at night. Meanwhile the mother builds her second nest and incubates the second brood. By the time the second brood hatches, the first brood is independent and has learned to flock with other young robins. The faithful father returns to the new nest to feed his new babies. The whole process will be repeated one more time during the summer.

Only about 40% of robin nests are successful in fledging babies, and only about 25% of fledged young survive their first summer. Robins face many dangers. Jays, crows, and squirrels eat robin eggs and nestlings. Many robins are killed by housecats, because robins often nest near human habitation and forage mostly on or near the ground where they are vulnerable to cats. Pesticides and herbicides, especially those used on lawns and agricultural fields where robins hunt for worms, can be deadly to robins. Most robins die in their first year. But if a young robin makes it through that first year, it has developed the skills to live much longer. The average first year survivor lives to be about six years old.

At the end of summer, robins gather in large flocks and begin to head south. As cold weather sets in, worms burrow below the frost, and insects become scarce. Winter robins range widely in search of berries and other fruits, and they roost in trees at night. Often a winter flock will number 100,000 or more birds and incorporate other fruit-eaters like mockingbirds, waxwings, and pine grosbeaks. Bird banding studies tell us that individual robins may winter in different places each year. A robin that spends this winter in Florida may spend next winter in Wisconsin. But in spring, all robins return to their nesting grounds.

Now, in late April, I've started to hear robins singing on Isle au Haut. There is something brave and inspiring about the way a robin chooses a conspicuous perch and sings his heart out, spreading good cheer over the neighborhood. It would be lovely if all of us would take time to acclaim the new season and, like the robin, find a high place to sing our praise.

Snowshoe Hares
(Lepus americanus)

Every spring when our lawn turns green, snowshoe hares come out of the forest early in the morning to feed in the new grass. After their spartan winter diet of bark, twigs, and buds it must be irresistible to eat something tender and fresh. They nibble on clover, dandelions, and whatever other shoots strike their fancy. They arrive a little nervously since they are quintessential prey animals and must always be wary of danger. But the sight of them hopping slowly along as they forage in the dawn light is peaceful and cheering.

Photo by John DeWitt

Hares and rabbits belong to the same taxonomic family, the lagomorphs. They resemble rodents in that their teeth are constantly growing and they need to chew continually to keep their teeth worn to the proper length. Hares are generally larger than rabbits, with longer legs and ears. Hares live singly and make shallow depressions called forms in which they rest, sleep, and bear young. The young are born fully furred and ready to leave the nest within hours of birth. Rabbits (except cottontails) live in colonies and make burrows. They are born naked, blind, and helpless, and stay in their burrows or nests for three or four weeks after birth. Hares are wild animals, while rabbits have been domesticated for meat, fur, and as pets.

The vegetarian diet of lagomorphs contains a lot of cellulose. Cellulose, the main component of plant cell walls, is difficult to digest. All grazing animals share this problem, and they have solved it with digestive system adaptations. Large grazers like deer and cattle have four-chambered stomachs to process cellulose. Lagomorphs are small, lightweight, and need to be able to flee predators quickly. Instead of adding bulky organs, they digest their food twice. The first time through, food is excreted as soft pellets rich in undigested nutrients. We never see these small, jelly-like pellets because hares re-ingest them as they are excreted, usually in the nest. The second time through, fully digested waste is expelled as the fibrous little pellets familiar to us as rabbit poop.

Snowshoe hares are native to the snowy regions of northern North America. They are camouflaged by turning white in the winter and brown in the summer. In early spring and late fall, you can see them in their patchy transitional pelage. They are named for their large hind feet, which are heavily furred, and have stiff hairs between the toes. In deep snow, the toes spread and act like snowshoes, preventing the hares from sinking in.

Snowshoe hares in Maine begin their breeding season in March. Gestation lasts about five weeks. Because a female hare, or doe, has a two-chambered uterus, she can become pregnant with a second litter before her first litter is born. Litters average four or five young called leverets. Many does bear three litters in a season. The leverets leave the nest within a day, but stay hidden nearby while their mother is away feeding. She returns to nurse her young once a day for a few minutes shortly after sunset, rapidly pumping out her nutritious milk. The leverets begin to forage within a week of their birth, are weaned in two to four weeks, and are completely independent by six weeks. Snowshoe hares have evolved to produce many offspring every summer because only about 15% survive their first year.

Snowshoe hare populations cycle roughly every ten years. A four or five year period of high population is followed by a period of population decline, and then a rebuilding to high levels again. In northernmost regions this fluctuation is huge; in downeast Maine it is less dramatic. Ecologists have yet to determine the causes of this population fluctuation, but research shows that approximately 95% of snowshoe hare deaths are caused by predation rather than disease or shortage of available food. Many leverets fall prey to red squirrels before they are weaned. Snowshoe hares are hunted by a daunting array of predators—coyotes, foxes, owls, hawks, weasels, mink, fisher, and lynx. Hares escape their predators by running, often zigzagging or leaping to throw off pursuit. They also rely on their cryptic coloration, sometimes freezing in their tracks to avoid being seen. Their lives are full of danger.

And yet, there are moments of safety. One spring morning I stood at my window watching two snowshoe hares grazing. A doe (deer) with two fawns walked into the yard. The doe quietly approached one of the hares, which showed no sign of alarm. The two animals touched noses and then, while the deer stood on her hind legs trying to eat the new leaves off our peach tree, the hares and the fawns played a game of chase. A fawn stalked closer and closer to a hare. The hare then bolted a short distance away and resumed feeding while the fawn began the game over again. The game lasted five magical minutes. Witnessing that moment in the peaceable kingdom taught me that the animals around us know each other well and can sometimes take respite with each other in spite of the dangers that surround them.

Vernal Pools

If you poke around in the woods in the early spring, you will find, here and there, a woodland pool reflecting the sky under the leafless trees. If you peer carefully into the water, you may see baseball-sized, gelatinous masses of eggs attached to underwater vegetation or fallen limbs. Where do these eggs come from, and why are they there? The answer lies in the nature of vernal pools.

After the dry heat of the summer, the New England woods are parched, and leaves crackle underfoot. But in the fall and winter, rain and snow and rising water tables cause water to pool and freeze in the low places. In the early spring, when the snow melts and the rains come, these woodland depressions brim full with water, forming vernal pools. Before the trees leaf out, the woods in early spring are dotted with these pools of various depths and sizes. As the weather warms, even the largest of these pools will dry up and disappear, but not before they play a crucial role in the lives of many amphibians.

Vernal pools are the breeding grounds for woodland frogs and salamanders, and for some smaller animals as well. Because vernal pools dry up, they do not support populations of fish. Without fish to prey on them, the frog and salamander eggs and young have an important advantage for their survival. On Isle au Haut, the species of amphibians using vernal pools for breeding include wood frogs, spring peepers, and spotted salamanders. Each one of these species has its unique mating rituals triggered by rising temperatures and wet conditions.

You have surely heard the mating calls of spring peepers, which fill the woods at night with their shrill cries during March and April. The duck-like quacking of wood frogs congregating in vernal pools is another sure sign of spring. And if you have ever gone out on the first warm, rainy night of April to watch the yellow-spotted salamanders make their yearly migration into the pools where they were born, you have seen one of the amazing phenomena of the New England springtime.

Once their eggs are laid, the adult frogs and salamanders leave the vernal pools to return to the forest. Now the eggs are in a race against time. They must hatch, and the young must mature from aquatic larvae with gills to air-breathing adults with lungs before their pool dries up. Even in a good year many are lost to predation. If the pool dries up too fast, thousands of tadpoles and salamander larvae will be exposed, wriggling in the muck of the drying pool bottom. These may become food for birds, snakes, squirrels, insects or just about any carnivore or omnivore that happens along.

But most years, enough of the little frogs and salamanders survive to replenish our woodland amphibian populations. The miniature frogs and salamanders disperse from the vernal pools into the woods where they begin their adult lives. The wood frogs and peepers shelter in the moist leaf litter, and the salamanders tunnel under the ground or keep moist under logs and rocks. All of them hunt invertebrates such as worms, insects, spiders, snails, and slugs. All of them will return to the same pools where they began their lives when they reach breeding age. We rarely see these animals even though they live close to us all year, but in the spring, we can catch a glimpse of their fascinating lives.

*D*andelions
(Taraxacum officinale)

When I was a girl I spent my summers on a farm in Vermont. Mabel, the mother of the farm family, assigned us chores. One of these chores was picking and—when Mabel was feeling especially ferocious—uprooting dandelions. Mabel was on a crusade against dandelions. She taught me that dandelions are unwelcome invaders in a decent lawn and must be opposed with force and diligence. Since then I have learned more about dandelions, and have made an uneasy peace with them. I still have irrational and, as you will see, impractical urges to eradicate them from my lawn, but I have come to admire and enjoy them.

Photo by John DeWitt

Dandelions are perennial plants with long, deeply toothed leaves that give them their name. "Dent de lion" means lion's tooth in French. Dandelions are native to

Eurasia, but have spread all over the world. They have long, deep taproots, most commonly from six to eighteen inches long. But an old plant in deep soil can penetrate up to fifteen feet into the earth. Dandelion leaves form a basal rosette. This means the leaves emerge from a central point on the ground, like the spokes of a wheel. The flowers, borne on hollow stems, also arise from the center. Dandelions are composite flowers. Each petal, or ray, is actually a simplified flower, which will form one seed. The ray flowers are all packed together on a single platform, the familiar little nubbin that is left when the seeds blow away. The flower goes to seed quickly, becoming a round, white, fluffy seedhead overnight. Each seed is carried off on its own tiny parachute, and can travel long distances in the wind.

Dandelions have many adaptations that help them to thrive despite human opposition. It is difficult to dig their long, brittle taproots without breaking them, and a new plant is generated by each broken piece of root. So the likelihood is that when you dig up a dandelion, you are helping it to proliferate. Dandelion seeds germinate without any period of dormancy, and the plants multiply freely every year. Also, dandelions do not need to be cross-pollinated. Each flower can fertilize itself, and thus is not dependent on insects or wind for pollination. And dandelions thrive in disturbed soil and lawns, so they naturally gravitate to human settlements. If you have dreams of getting rid of dandelions, dream on. They are here, and in your lawn, to stay.

But wait. Dandelions are actually good for your lawn. Their deep taproots aerate the soil and bring nutrients from deep underground to the surface. Their cheerful flowers announce spring all over the countryside. And they are among the most versatile of medicinal plants. They have been used for millennia to cure many ailments, from liver dysfunction to warts. They are a mild diuretic and digestive aid. Dandelion leaves can be collected and eaten fresh, the earlier in the spring the better. They have more vitamin C than tomatoes, and are rich in iron and calcium, as well as vitamins A, B, E and K. The flowers can be used to make wine, and the ground-up roots are a caffeine-free coffee substitute. If you were to decide to grow dandelions for sale, ground dandelion roots fetch about $30 per pound—more than lobster or swordfish or filet mignon. If you can't beat 'em, join 'em.

Last, but not least, dandelions are beloved of children. Everyone remembers blowing dandelion puffballs and watching the seeds float in the wind. The number of blows can tell you how many years until you get married, how many children you will have, how often your lover is thinking of you. You can make a wish on a flying seed—if you can catch it! And dandelion flowers can be picked everywhere—no one ever got scolded for picking a dandelion. So next time a child presents you with a cheerful yellow bouquet of dandelions, maybe you can give thanks for this common, irrepressible weed.

Spring Warblers

The spring warbler migration is a highlight of any birdwatcher's year. Though many people have never noticed warblers, more than twenty species migrate along the coast of Maine in the spring. They come in flocks, and their bright colors, distinctive songs, and constant activity in the treetops provide an opportunity for anyone with a pair of binoculars to observe them.

Warblers are small, brightly colored songbirds that winter in the southern United States, the Caribbean, and Central and South America. In spring they flood northward in mixed flocks on their way to breeding grounds as far north as Labrador. They come in waves, taking advantage of southerly winds. The first migrants reach Maine in April, and by mid-May you may see as many as ten or twelve species in one tree singing and feeding. Their plumage is most often yellow and olive accentuated with black, white, blue, gray, orange or red markings. Each species has distinctive plumage and a unique song. Many birders can unerringly identify all our spring warblers by ear.

Birds migrate north to take advantage of open nesting territories and abundant summer food. Migrating birds consume huge amounts of energy in long distance travel. Some warblers cross the Gulf of Mexico, flying non-stop for four days. During that marathon, a warbler can lose as much as half its body weight. It makes landfall exhausted and literally starving, and must feed or die. Throughout their migration warblers fly all night, and at dawn must find a place to rest and refuel. They look for stands of trees, preferring trees that are leafing out and flowering, because these trees attract so many insects. The warblers often stay a few days before moving on.

Warblers are insectivorous. Insects are attracted to the inconspicuous flowers of oaks, maples, birches, poplars, and many other early spring flowering trees. Warblers feed busily in the trees, especially in the morning hours when the sun warms the treetops and insects become active. Warblers gobble masses of caterpillars that are emerging in the unfolding leaves, thus protecting the crowns of our awakening hardwoods from devastation by caterpillars.

While feeding, male warblers proclaim themselves in song. The basic purpose of birdsong is to establish, advertise, and defend nesting territories. However, male warblers, and many other migrating songbirds, sing extravagantly during migration before arriving at their breeding grounds. Males usually migrate before females in order to establish nesting territories before the females arrive. Birders especially enjoy flocks of primarily male warblers because of their conspicuous breeding plumage and the variety of their high-pitched, trilling songs. Later in the spring the females migrate through. Females are harder to identify because their plumage is duller and they do not sing.

As the migration moves north, individual warblers gravitate to their particular nesting habitats, and the flocks begin to disperse. Warblers are songbirds that nest in our forests, shrublands, and marshes. Some species, like the yellow-rumped warbler and the common yellowthroat, are generalists, able to nest in a variety of habitats. Others, like yellow and bay-breasted warblers, are specialists, needing access to very particular habitats. Most warblers are monogamous. Males stake out territories by singing around the perimeter of their claim and driving off rivals. When the females arrive, they check out the territories of various males, listen to their songs, and select mates. Courtship, mating, and nest-building quickly ensue.

The female warbler builds the nest and incubates the eggs while the male feeds her. The chicks hatch naked, blind, and unable to regulate their body temperatures. Within a few days they begin to grow feathers. They develop quickly, and leave the nest at eight to twelve days old. The parents continue to feed them outside the nest for about a month, at which time the young become independent. Most warblers nesting in the north raise only one brood. On Isle au Haut, our signature nesting warbler is the black-throated green warbler. We hear its songs all summer from the spruce forest—"zoo-zee, zoo-zoo zee," and "zee-zee-zee zoo-zee"—as it goes about the business of nesting.

Before the warblers leave us in the fall they undergo a molt into drab winter plumage. They seldom sing as they move south, and the adults are mixed with immature birds whose plumage is different from that of their elders. All these factors make warblers much more challenging to identify in the fall than in the spring. The fall warblers gather again into mixed flocks, feeding voraciously before the long haul of migration south to warmer climates.

But in the spring, especially on nights with a south wind, a river of birds is flowing northward high above us. If you are lucky, you might see a flock of them silhouetted against the full moon as they pass. In the morning, that river of birds comes down. If you take time to look, you may find the flowering trees in your neighborhood transformed by the presence of warblers as they pursue food and get ready for nesting season. Watch for them now. Soon they will be gone.

Tide Pools and the Intertidal Zone

Here on Isle au Haut we have ten-foot tides. When I look out my window, the view between me and the York Island a half a mile distant varies dramatically depending on where we are in the tide cycle. At high tide I see an expanse of water broken only by a few knobs of gray rock. At low tide I see myriad ledges draped with rockweed, some rising from sandy beaches and some containing pools of seawater. The area that is covered and uncovered in the regular rhythm of the tides is called the intertidal zone.

Photo by Marnie Davis

Looking at the expanse of the intertidal area at low tide, one can see different life zones, which are determined by the amount of time each zone spends underwater as the tide rises and falls. The zone closest to the high tide line is the most stressful environment, and only a few animals and plants can survive there. In this high intertidal zone we see rocks darkened by a slick of algae. Below the high intertidal zone is a white band of barnacles, which escape predation by living where no predator can get to them. Below the barnacle zone, a brown expanse of rockweed covers the rocks. The lowest zone in the intertidal is a band of reddish seaweed called the red zone. Below the red zone, completely submerged in all but the lowest tides, are forests of kelp.

The plants and animals that live in the rocky intertidal have adapted to withstand the rigors of a challenging and highly variable environment. Imagine living in a place that is flooded and then exposed twice a day. You face extremes of temperature—both daily and seasonally—and strong, drying winds during the hours of exposure. When the tide floods in, you must hold on for dear life to avoid being swept away by waves and currents. But the intertidal zone offers shelter in the form of tide pools. Tide pools form anywhere where rocky hollows trap seawater when the tide ebbs. Tide pools can be shallow puddles, deep clefts, or large troughs. They provide living space for many plants and animals that cannot survive on exposed rock.

A tide pool is like a natural aquarium in the rocks. It provides marine organisms with a place to stay wet, regulate their temperature, find food, and hide. It may be home to many different seaweeds and animals. The diversity of life in a tide pool depends on where it is in the intertidal zone. The tide pools with the greatest biodiversity are down in the red zone. These pools are completely submerged for long periods twice a day as inrushing seawater, oxygenated by wave action, floods and overwhelms them. Then, at low tide, they become safe havens where life can proceed in water that is calm and saturated with life-giving oxygen.

Exploring a big tide pool in the red zone is a fascinating pursuit. You can find a variety of seaweeds and animals—and sometimes it is hard to tell which is which. As in any ecosystem, there are plants, the primary producers, making their own food from water, air, and sunlight. In this case all the plants are marine algae, better known as seaweeds. They come in three types—green, red, and brown, and they exhibit an amazing variety of size and structure. There are flat, delicate, green sea lettuces, long brown strands of rockweed, red fronds of dulse, heavy brown ribbons of kelp, and many kinds of filamentous algae in all three colors. Pink patches called crustose algae encrust rocks and shells. Coralline algae, which look like tiny branching corals, wave gently among the bigger seaweeds. All seaweeds in the intertidal have a leaf-like part and a structure called a holdfast with which they cling to the rock or other substrate, so that they will not be swept away.

If you are patient you can find a profusion of animals that feed on the seaweeds and on each other. Periwinkles, limpets, sea urchins and other herbivores graze peacefully over the rocks and seaweeds. Filter feeders like sponges, mussels, and clams draw seawater into their bodies and strain out tiny particles of nutrition. Barnacles comb the water with rake-like arms called cirri, collecting food. Starfish and dog whelks hunt their favored prey species. Crabs scavenge busily. You may see a hermit crab scuttle over the bottom in the shell of a periwinkle, or an anemone flaring its frilly mouth as it waits for small prey. Multitudes of tiny shrimplike creatures called amphipods zip through the water in pursuit of dead or dying animals and seaweed. If you lift a curtain of rockweed, you might find clusters of snail eggs attached to the rocks, or strange-looking worms covered with tiny scales.

Each one of these animals has a unique way of life, but they all have at least one thing in common. They must all attach themselves to the rocks or hide in deep cracks when the rising tide surges in. If you are going tidepooling, be sure to check a tide chart and arrive at least an hour before the tide turns. Watch for incoming waves, and make your getaway over the slippery rocks and seaweeds when the ocean begins to surge into the pool. The waves can knock you down. You are not as well adapted to tide pool life as the plants and animals that live there.

June Bugs

(*Phyllophaga* spp.)

I dug up some new garden space this spring by removing an area of thick grass with deep and fibrous roots. It was a strenuous job, and in the process I encountered numerous large white grubs among the roots in the sandy soil. Every year I unearth these grubs, which are the larval form of June bugs. Last fall I learned that the holes eaten in my potatoes while they are growing underground—holes I had always unfairly attributed to voles—are made by grubs. I discovered this when I was digging potatoes and caught a grub in the act of gouging its characteristic hole in one of my precious spuds. Since that moment of revelation, I have become a ruthless grub-squasher, leaving an unceremoniously discarded trail of deflated white bodies in my wake as I dig.

June bugs are beetles. Beetles are an order of insects called Coleoptera, which are the most successful multicellular animals on the planet. There are about 450,000 known species of beetles. If we count yet-to-be-discovered species, there are probably more than a million. The word Coleoptera comes from the Greek words for "sheathed wing." Most beetles have two pairs of wings, one of which consists of hard sheaths called elytra that cover the delicate flying wings and protect the beetle's body. If you have ever watched a ladybug take flight and land (in typical beetle fashion), you have seen it open its wing covers, extend its wings and fly away, and then, as it lands fold its wings and close the wing covers. Often the trailing edges of the wings are incompletely folded and protrude from underneath the covers for a while until the ladybug finishes tucking them away.

Beetles, like most insects, have a life cycle called complete metamorphosis. This means they have four life stages: the egg, the larva, the pupa, and the adult. The egg is laid by an adult female insect. The egg hatches into a tiny larva, which is primarily an eating machine. Its purpose is to grow. As it grows it sheds its skin many times, passing through a new growth stage, or instar, each time it molts. We are all familiar with several forms of larvae. Grubs, maggots, and caterpillars are all larval insects. There are more larval forms we do not recognize—as many as there are forms of adult insects. When the larva has achieved its full growth, it stops eating and pupates, shedding its last larval skin and taking a new form. The pupa is the mysterious vessel in which the insect body rearranges itself from a larva into an adult. When this process is complete, the new adult breaks the pupal skin, inflates its wings (if it is a winged insect), and begins its adult life. The adult is the reproductive stage of the insect, responsible for mating, laying eggs, and thus beginning the next generation.

There are more than 250 species of June bugs. The species most familiar to us is the large, ungainly, reddish beetle that buzzes around, sometimes in multitudes, on spring nights. June bugs are attracted to light, and often crash repeatedly into windows or hang on screens where, if you want, you can take a close look at their shiny, rounded bodies. Adult June bugs have spent the winter in underground burrows below the frost line. In spring they come to the surface, spending the days resting a few inches beneath the soil surface. They emerge at dusk to feed on leaves and look for mates. The females emit a pheromone that immediately attracts all the males within a 20-yard radius. After mating, females deposit their eggs in small clods of earth up to seven inches underground.

The eggs hatch in two to four weeks, and the new little larvae feed on vegetable matter in the soil all summer. In the fall, larger but not yet full-grown, the larvae will burrow down below the frost to await another spring. It is during their second season as larvae that white grubs do the most damage. These second-year larvae are the largest grubs in the soil, up to an inch long and curled into a C-shape. They feed on the roots of plants. They favor grains and other grasses, but also consume the roots of crops including corn, strawberries, and potatoes. At the end of this second summer, the larvae pupate deep in the soil. They press against the surrounding earth, creating ovoid underground cells in which they change into brown-skinned pupae. The adult beetles hatch in a few weeks, but remain underground throughout the fall and winter, emerging at last as adults in their third spring.

The damage done by white grubs tends to be in three-year cycles. Two summers after a heavy infestation of June bug adults, many large white grubs are feeding just beneath the soil surface. Last year on Isle au Haut was one of those summers. There were lawns all over the island that developed large brown patches in August. The dry turf could be peeled up like a rug, its roots completely severed by the grubs, which lay scattered like big white commas on the exposed ground beneath. Crows, recognizing an easy meal, descended on the brown patches, turning them up and eating all the grubs. Nothing was left but torn shreds of dead turf littering the bare earth.

Being humans, with our mammalian experience of development as a slow trajectory from little and helpless to big and independent, we are unaccustomed to the development strategies of many other animals. For the majority of our fellow creatures, development is a punctuated process in which immature forms have different appearances, behaviors, foods, and habitats from their parents. Despite my murderous attacks on the white grubs in my garden, I like knowing where they came from and what they would have become had I not rudely interrupted their lives.

Atlantic Puffins
(Fraturcula arctica)

Part 1: Puffins at Seal Island

Last weekend I was the naturalist aboard the Isle au Haut Mailboat, the Mink, on a birdwatching trip to Seal Island. Puffins, razorbills, black guillemots, eider ducks, Leach's storm petrels, great cormorants, double-crested cormorants, common terns, Arctic terns, and several species of gulls all nest on Seal Island. It was a perfect day for a sea journey, warm and clear without much swell or wind. The island was thronged with seabirds—floating, flying, perched on rocks, setting on nests. If we had made this same voyage fifteen years ago, we would have seen no puffins, no razorbills, no terns. How has this remarkable change happened?

Photo by Marnie Davis

Seal Island is a narrow comma of rock about a mile long, located eight miles east of Matinicus. It has no mammalian predators and includes sixty-five acres of grassland, rock ledge, and boulders. This variety of safe nesting habitats makes Seal

Island an ideal seabird nesting site. In the mid 19th century, Seal Island supported the largest puffin colony in the Gulf of Maine.

In those days, mariners landed on the island to hunt seabirds and gather eggs for food. Collectors also killed seabirds to acquire feathers for the millinery trade. In 1887 the last puffins nesting on Seal Island were killed. Not coincidentally, the National Audubon Society was founded in 1886 in response to the alarming slaughter of millions of birds, particularly egrets, for ladies' hats. This was the beginning of the American movement to protect birds. By the early 20th century only two Maine islands, Matinicus Rock and Machias Seal Island (not the Seal Island we visited last week), had colonies of puffins. Atlantic puffins were abundant only in remote areas of northern Canada and Newfoundland, where the majority of them still live today.

By the middle of the 20th century, the U.S. Navy owned Seal Island. The Navy used it as a bombing range from the 1940s until the 1960s. Because there is still unexploded ordnance on the island, unauthorized landing is prohibited, though now there is a small group of scientists living on the island studying puffins and other nesting birds during the breeding season. In 1972, Seal Island became a part of the Maine Coastal Islands National Wildlife Refuge, which consists of more than 40 islands and some mainland coastal zones. A primary objective of the Refuge is to restore breeding populations of seabirds.

In 1973 Steve Kress, a Cornell graduate student supported by the National Audubon Society, began Project Puffin. Kress was passionate about seabirds and wanted to protect and strengthen seabird populations. Project Puffin's goal is to return puffins to their traditional nesting sites in the Gulf of Maine. Kress chose Eastern Egg Rock near Pemaquid as the first reintroduction site for puffins. Kress knew that puffins naturally return to nest on the island where they fledged. He believed scientists might reintroduce puffins by raising puffin chicks, called pufflings, on Eastern Egg Rock and waiting for them to return. Kress's first puffin chicks came from Great Island, Newfoundland, home to more than 160,000 pairs of puffins. The first year, the project raised only six chicks. The next year Newfoundland donated 54 more chicks. After that Kress transplanted 100 chicks each spring.

Puffins dig long burrows, either under boulders or in turf, where they raise their chicks. Kress's team constructed artificial sod burrows on the island. They transplanted ten-day-old pufflings into the burrows. The pufflings were old enough to toddle out to the mouth of the burrow to eat. Kress's team fed the chicks for a month, leaving a small heap of fish at the mouth of each burrow daily, but never permitting visual contact between the pufflings and their benefactors. The first year all six chicks fledged successfully. The scientists settled down to wait for their return.

Every year Kress's team introduced more chicks, and continued to wait. They placed puffin decoys on the tops of boulders each spring to attract returning birds, and played recordings of puffin vocalizations. They also mounted a program to control the population of predatory gulls in anticipation of the puffins' return. Finally, in 1977, puffins began to return to Eastern Egg Rock. Imagine the joy of the scientists as they watched the birds they had raised years before come home to nest.

Puffins are pelagic birds, which means they live their entire lives at sea, coming to land only to nest and raise their young. Puffins live to be more than 20 years old. It takes three to five years for a young puffin to become sexually mature. That's why it took so long for the puffins to come back.

In 1984, the National Audubon Society initiated a similar project on Seal Island, and in 1992 the first puffins returned. Seal Island is now the largest colony of puffins in Maine, with over 500 nesting pairs. Project Puffin has become a model for seabird restoration around the world. The only time we can see puffins is from late April through mid-August. After August, the nesting phase is complete and the puffins return to the sea.

It is a great thrill to visit a nesting island. You head out to sea, and when you first see the island, it is a dot on the horizon. As you approach, you begin to encounter individual birds—terns, gulls, puffins—and as you get close, the individuals become a multitude, everywhere you look. The sound of them fills the air. You have arrived at a place where humans are rarely privileged to be.

Part 2: The Lives of Puffins

It is hard to imagine the lives of puffins and other offshore seabirds. Their journeys rarely bring them in sight of land. For a few short months in the spring and summer they come to remote islands or shores to breed. Then they disperse again to the open ocean, a habitat that seems to any landlubber a trackless expanse devoid of reference points or destinations. This makes it difficult to study these birds at sea, or even to discover where they spend their time when they are not nesting

Puffins' bodies are adapted in many ways to meet the challenges of living at sea. First, they are phenomenal divers. They pursue fish for themselves and their young by literally flying underwater, using their short, rounded wings for propulsion and their webbed feet for steering. They catch small fish such as herring, hake, capelin and sand lance. They achieve depths of over 200 feet when hunting. Puffins can withstand the enormous pressure of water in the depths, and adjust quickly to atmospheric pressure as they resurface. In similar circumstances, humans would die of the bends. Puffins are sight hunters, yet they must be able to locate prey at depths where there is little ambient light. We do not know how they follow prey in deep water.

Scientists believe that puffins at sea locate areas where prey is abundant by looking for concentrations of phytoplankton, the single-celled plants that are the basis of the ocean food web. Where there is phytoplankton, there is zooplankton, the tiny animals that feed on phytoplankton. Where there is zooplankton there are small fish feeding and that makes good hunting for puffins. Puffins also find areas where currents flowing over shoals and banks concentrate prey, or where opposing currents cause upwellings of nutrients that attract prey.

Puffins must drink seawater since they have no access to fresh water. Like many seabirds, they are equipped with salt glands. Salt glands are organs located in the skull above the eyes. Their function is to absorb excess salt from the blood. The puffins sneeze out the excess salt, which drips down channels in their beaks and falls away.

Though they are well adapted for underwater flight, puffins' stubby, short wings and chunky bodies make flying in the air a high-energy activity. In the past scientists have speculated that puffins must winter somewhere near their nesting islands. Recently, researchers have trapped puffins on their breeding grounds at Seal Island and attached tiny geolocators to their legs in order to determine where they go in the winter. Tagged birds must be recaptured the following year to download data from the devices—a difficult task. But we are learning that puffins are far-ranging birds. One of the recaptured geolocators showed that "Cabot," the puffin that carried it, had traveled north to the Labrador Sea, south to the mid-Atlantic, and finally back to Seal Island, an amazing eight-month journey of 4,800 miles, all on those stubby little wings.

As springtime approaches, puffins molt into their elegant black-and-white breeding plumage. Their beaks, which have been dull orange all winter, change to bright red and orange. Puffins are monogamous, though couples do not stay together all year. Each bird must reunite with its mate somewhere near their nesting island after the long winter separation. After arriving at the nesting island, puffins court by rubbing their colorful beaks together, and then mate. Puffins nest in deep crevices among the boulders, or dig three-foot long burrows into sod. They often use the same crevice or burrow year after year. The female lays one egg in a nest chamber at the end of the burrow. Puffins are colonial nesters, and a colony may have thousands of nests all in close proximity.

Puffin parents share the chore of incubating their egg. The puffling hatches after six weeks. It is covered in blackish down, which means it can stay warm by itself while both parents hunt for food. The parents hunt at sea and bring food to the puffling in the burrow for six weeks. A puffin can carry up to thirty fish in its bill. It uses its spiky tongue to press fish it has caught against the top mandible, which leaves the bottom mandible free to snap up more fish. The chick must get quite fat, because the parents, eager to return to the sea, stop feeding it about a week before it fledges.

After the parents leave, the puffling, who must be getting hungrier and hungrier, waddles out of the burrow at dusk, jumps from the rocks into the sea, and swims away. It must immediately begin to hunt on its own—a steep learning curve, to say the least. It flies for the first time about ten days later. It will be years before the puffling returns to the nesting island. A young puffin stays at sea for four or five years until it is sexually mature. Only then will it seek a mate and return to land once more. Puffins' average lifespan in the wild is 25 years. Though puffins raise only one chick per year, a pair of puffins can raise many chicks during a lifetime.

Ominously, in 2012 and 2013, nesting success for puffins on Seal Island plummeted from its normal average of 77 percent. In 2012 only 31 percent of pufflings survived. In 2013, the survival rate was down to 10 percent. This seems to be the result of rapid warming in the waters of the Gulf of Maine. This warming has changed the abundance of puffins' primary food species, hake and herring, and has encouraged the abundance of other less suitable species such as butterfish, which are too big for the baby puffins. In 2012, many pufflings died amidst piles of butterfish, which was the only species of fish their parents could find to bring to them. Perhaps more alarming, the warmer waters are interfering with spring blooms of phytoplankton which are the base of ocean food webs. In fact, the 2013 spring bloom of phytoplankton was so small it was undetectable by scientific instruments used to monitor the Gulf of Maine. That's a little like saying that all the grasses of the Serengeti Plains failed to grow this year. No wonder puffins had a hard time finding food for their young. In the complex ecosystem of the Gulf of Maine, the consequences of the collapse of phytoplankton are beyond imagination. Two years do not provide enough data to be conclusive about the future of puffins, but based on predictions of the course of global warming, we have a lot to worry about.

For now, we still have puffins nesting on Seal Island, and we still have hope. The sweet faces, colorful beaks, orange feet, and interesting behavior of puffins charm the lucky people who have a chance to visit their nesting islands. Some people call them "clowns of the sea" because they are so much fun to watch. The closest breeding island to Isle au Haut is Seal Island, about 25 miles south of Stonington. The Isle au Haut Mailboat has three puffin cruises every summer. Welcome aboard!

Earthworms

(Lumbricidae)

One of the pleasures of digging in the spring garden is turning up a multitude of healthy, wriggling earthworms with each forkful of dirt. During the long winter, worms retreat beneath the frostline to avoid death by freezing. They gather in the cold soil in tangled balls and wait for the layer of frozen soil above them to melt. When at last the ground thaws they resurface and return to their work of tilling, aerating, and enriching the soil.

Worms are decomposers, feeding on undecayed plant material. They pass soil through their long, tubular bodies and break down the organic matter it contains. They carry dead leaves and other plant detritus from the soil surface underground. They also bring soil from underground up to the surface where they eject little squiggles of digested earth called castings. These castings are rich in organic matter and nutrients valuable to plants. Charles Darwin, who studied earthworms extensively for many years, estimated that on an average acre of cultivated land 16,000 pounds of earth are brought to the surface by worms each year.

Worms move underground by alternately contracting and extending their bodies, which are constructed of a series of muscular rings around a digestive tube and blood vessels in the center. Each ring is equipped with bristles angled backwards. These bristles hold the worm's position so that it can push forward through the soil. As they move through the soil, worms create tunnels through which water and air, vital to plant roots and soil organisms, can percolate into the earth. The burrowing process is facilitated by the worm's production of mucus, which lubricates both the worm and its tunnels.

Worms are hermaphrodites. Each worm is equipped with male and female organs that are located near the enlarged band called the clitellum near the head end of a mature worm. But a worm cannot fertilize itself. It must find a partner. Two worms meet head to head and slide next to each other until each worm's head is just past the other worm's clitellum. Then the worms pass sperm to each other. The eggs are not fertilized until later. Once fertilization takes place, each worm secretes cocoons with eggs inside and deposits them in the earth on or near the surface. Tiny worms hatch inside the cocoons and wiggle out into the soil. It takes several months for a worm to become sexually mature, and as much as a year to attain its full size. Worms may live as long as eight years, but most garden worms have a lifespan of about two years.

The worms we all see in our yards and gardens are not native to the Americas. The last glaciation, which ended about 12,000 years ago, wiped out almost all species of North American earthworms. It was not until European settlers arrived bringing many plants and their rootballs that the earthworms we know today became established here. These worms have helped the fertility of our fields and gardens, but are interfering with the ecology of our forests.

After the glaciers retreated, North American forests evolved without worms, and developed deep layers of duff, the thick layer of leaf litter that builds up on the forest floor. Non-native earthworms, which in our forests are classified as invasive species, quickly convert duff into topsoil, which changes the conditions in which native wildflowers, ferns, and saplings must grow. Many native plants cannot survive without duff. The good news is that unless people transport worms, they move into new areas very slowly. So, if you are a fisherman, please don't dump your bait worms by woodland ponds and streams. The worms we love in our gardens can do harm in our forests.

Carnivorous Plants

Isle au Haut is a boggy place. Bogs are acidic wetlands common across the entire northern tier of the planet, where glaciers have scoured soils and carved rocks, leaving depressions that hold water. Dead organic matter sinks to the bottom of these pools and decomposes, creating acidic conditions. Sphagnum mosses thrive in these acidic, nutrient-deprived, oxygen-poor environments, adding to the acidity of the bog water when they decay. All plants and animals that live in bogs must have special adaptations to obtain the sustenance they need in this challenging environment. Bog plants are specialized to survive in places where most plants would quickly die from lack of nitrogen and other nutrients. Carnivorous plants are among the most fascinating and beautiful of these resourceful plants.

Pitcher Plant - Photo by Marnie Davis

In late June and early July, I often take time to stop at local bogs and look out over the characteristic expanse of sphagnum moss, sedges, grasses, skunk cabbage, low shrubs, and stunted trees. Our bogs in summer are beautiful, colorful places decorated by the tall, red flowers of pitcher plants, carpeted by the red leaves of sundews, and patched with the brilliant yellow flowers of bladderworts. These three common groups of bog plants all meet some of their nutritional needs by consuming insects, and each group has a unique strategy for capturing its prey.

Pitcher plants have evolved six-inch tall leaves that are curled into hollow cups that act as pitfall traps for insects. Pitcher plants are usually rooted in sphagnum moss. The leaves of the pitcher plant form a basal rosette, which means that all the leaves emanate from a central point at ground or water level. Each pitcher plant leaf catches and holds rainwater into which the leaf secretes digestive enzymes. Pitcher plant leaves, which produce a fragrant nectar, are strikingly patterned with deep purple veins. Both these features attract insects to land on the curved lip of the pitcher. Moths, ants, wasps, and gnats are common prey. The lip and the entire inner surface of the pitcher plant leaf are covered with tiny hairs that point downward in a slippery slope towards the water-filled chamber. It is easy for an insect to slide down into the pitcher and difficult for it to climb out against the grain. Once in the water, the insect is dissolved by the pitcher's enzymes, and its nutrients become available to the pitcher plant.

There are a few insects that have evolved to take advantage of the pitcher plant's lifestyle rather than becoming its prey. A species of mosquito lays its eggs in the water inside the pitchers. Its larvae are unaffected by the digestive enzymes of the pitcher plant and develop in a safe haven with no predators. The larvae overwinter frozen inside the pitcher, and hatch out in the spring. There is also a species of fly whose larvae feed on leftover insect parts floating inside pitcher plant leaves.

Sundews are the second group of carnivorous plants. They are much smaller and more numerous than pitcher plants. Like pitcher plants, sundews are basal rosettes. Sundews grow in masses, forming a flat, red mat of vegetation in watery areas of the bog. A single sundew plant is about three inches in diameter. Each of its many leaves is covered with tiny red hairs, and each hair is tipped with a globule of sticky fluid. Sundews literally sparkle as if with thousands of tiny drops of dew, the characteristic that gives the sundew its name. Any small flying insect that blunders into a sundew leaf finds itself in the grip of the plant's natural flypaper. The struggling insect triggers the leaf to produce more sticky juice. The leaf hairs bend towards the insect to grasp it more firmly. Meanwhile, the sundew produces another enzyme that anaesthetizes the trapped insect. Within hours the insect is digested and incorporated by the sundew.

Bladderworts comprise the third group of carnivorous plants that are common in New England. These unusual plants have no roots. Their leaves float on or near the surface of bog water, forming a web. The bright yellow flower stands on a stem rising from the floating leaves. All along the net of finely divided leaves are tiny bladders, which scientists long assumed acted as flotation for the plant. We now know that each of these bean-shaped bladders is actually a trap for tiny aquatic organisms.

Sundew - Photo by John DeWitt

Depending on the species of bladderwort, the bladders are anywhere from one-thousandth to one-half an inch long. Each bladder is like a sealed sac, very thin and transparent but stiff enough to hold its shape under pressure. The seal is created by a trigger-activated trap door. When the door is closed, the cells in the walls of the bladder actively pump water out of the bladder, creating a partial vacuum inside. This pumping is accomplished by a cellular process called active transport in which the cell's energy is used to drive the pump and evacuate the water.

When the cells in the bladder's walls have pumped as much water as possible out of the bladder, the trap is set. Any tiny, swimming organism that brushes against the trigger causes the trap door to spring open. Water rushes in to fill the vacuum, carrying the prey animal along with it. Once the pressure is equalized, the trap door closes. The tiny organism is digested, and the bladder once more actively pumps out its water, creating another vacuum and priming the trap for its next victim.

Bogs are examples of specialized environments that inspire some of the most ingenious adaptations in nature. For carnivorous plants, capturing prey is not absolutely essential. The plants can survive by photosynthesis alone. But they flourish with the additional nutrients provided by their prey. Capturing and digesting tiny, nutritious creatures provides carnivorous plants with added nutrition that enables them to achieve maximum size, to flower vigorously and to set robust seeds. Pitfall traps, flypaper traps, and suction traps all evolved separately, but each evolutionary path was driven by the advantage provided by supplemental nutrition in an impoverished ecosystem.

Birdsong

When I step outside in the early morning to let my chickens out of their henhouse, I am greeted by birds singing all around me—the dawn chorus. A winter wren nesting in the spruce forest to our west sings his long, high-pitched, melodious song. A white-throated sparrow holds forth in the brushy meadow to our east with his signature whistle: "old Sam Peabody, Peabody, Peabody." A common yellowthroat sings "witchedy, witchedy, witchedy" down the hill to the south. The slow, soft trill of a yellow-rumped warbler comes from a big spruce near our fruit garden. The familiar clear notes and buzzy trills of song sparrows rise from all directions. And the air is filled with the burbling songs of purple finches that nest here in abundance. All summer the finches take advantage of our feeders and keep me entertained with song while I work in the garden.

Birdsong is an avian form of communication. Vocal communication among birds comes in two forms: songs and calls. Ornithologists generally differentiate songs and calls by their length and complexity as well as by their purpose. Songs tend to be longer, and serve to announce territoriality and attract mates. Calls tend to be brief and serve specific functions. There are alarm calls, contact calls, flight calls to keep a flock together, calls to pinpoint food sources, and the begging calls of young birds asking to be fed. Calls are innate—birds know them instinctively—while songs are usually learned from parents. And while almost all bird species have calls, song is characteristic of the perching birds better known as songbirds.

In general, the songs we hear during the nesting season at dawn and less frequently during the day are produced by male birds. Each species has a specific and recognizable song that serves the dual purpose of proclaiming territory and attracting a mate. This is why we hear so much birdsong in the early spring as migratory birds arrive. In most migratory species, males precede females in order to establish nesting territories. The males with the loudest songs and the most aggressive behaviors secure the best territories. When the females arrive, the same songs that warned other males to keep away serve to attract females who are choosing mates. Often the quality and frequency of the male's song is a sign of the breeding fitness of the singer. A male with a louder or more complex song is advertising his experience and his abilities, and is an attractive choice for a discerning female.

Once the pair bond has been established, the male continues to sing many times a day to remind other birds of the same species to respect his territory. Individual variation among the songs of males allows birds of the same species to distinguish a neighbor with an adjoining territory from an intruding stranger who might threaten the established territorial order. The intruding stranger quickly provokes a physical and vocal attack, while the neighbor is ignored. Thus the territorial male can conserve his energy for threats without having to investigate every nearby song.

Birdsong originates in a special muscular organ called the syrinx located deep in a bird's chest. The syrinx sits right where the bird's trachea divides in an upside down Y into the bronchial tubes that lead to each lung. Because of its location, the syrinx creates a resonating chamber in the bird's breast. When a bird wants to sing, it flexes the syrinx muscles on one or both sides of the Y, squeezing the air that is passing through. A bird has exquisite control of these muscles, and is able to produce precise variations in pitch and intensity of sounds. Some birds, such as thrushes and mockingbirds, can use both sides of the syrinx at once, creating the haunting harmonics that characterize their songs.

In some songbirds, such as flycatchers, song is innate and does not need to be learned, but most species learn their songs from adult teachers. The male nestling hatches with only a rudimentary song. As he listens to his father and other members of his species, his song develops increasing fidelity and structure until at last it becomes "crystallized." A young song sparrow raised in the presence of a white-throated sparrow will learn the white-throated sparrow's song instead of its own. But if he is raised in the presence of both a white-throated sparrow and a song sparrow, he will show preference for his specific song and will sing like other song sparrows. Interestingly, this means that in some species, the song is regional. Western song sparrows, for instance, have songs that are recognizable as song sparrow songs, but differ from those of eastern song sparrows.

Many birds develop repertoires of multiple songs as they mature and continue to learn. The North American champion of song repertoires is the brown thrasher, a relative of the mockingbird and the catbird—both also prodigious singers. He sings as many as 3,000 different songs. Birds like the brown thrasher, the catbird, and the mockingbird are part of a bird family called the mimids, or mimics. They learn new songs by imitating other birds. They are continually learning new phrases, which they incorporate into their long, complex songs. Thus the song of any individual mimic depends on what other birds live nearby—you may even hear some tropical strains learned in their winter homes. You can easily tell our three mimics apart. The mockingbird sings each phrase multiple times, the brown thrasher always repeats each phrase twice, and the catbird, with its series of warbles, squeaks and mews, sings each phrase only once.

When you step outdoors on a spring or early summer morning, stop a minute and listen. You will be hearing the conversations of the many birds who share your habitat with you. Depending on where you live—inland or near the coast, in a city, a suburb, or a wild remote area, you will hear different species. Birds are everywhere, announcing their presence. If you listen and observe carefully, you can learn to recognize the songs of your neighbors and take pleasure in their presence.

Daisies
(Leucanthemum vulgare)

One of my favorite wildflowers is the common oxeye daisy, which blooms prolifically on the roadsides and fields of coastal Maine at this time of year. When the daisies start to bloom a feeling of summer comes over me like a promise. Daisies nodding their pretty heads in the wind seem to say, "It's warm, and it's going to stay warm, and it's delightful to be out in the weather. Come on!"

Photo by John DeWitt

Our daisy is actually native to Europe and Asia. It arrived in America with European settlers and has become such a familiar part of our landscape that we think of it as belonging here, though in some states, especially where cattle are grazed, it is considered an invasive weed. The daisy is a generalist, which means it can grow in many different conditions—dry fields, meadows, scrubby areas, and even forests with enough light coming through the canopy. It produces an abundance of seeds, and also propagates with creeping underground roots. It especially likes disturbed areas like roadsides and waste places, where it can take hold and spread quickly.

Like the daisy, many of our most common wild plants hitchhiked from Europe or Asia with settlers, sometimes as seeds hidden in ship's ballast or animal bedding, sometimes as treasured reminders of home. These plants went to seed, escaping barns, gardens, and trash heaps, and spread over the landscape. We call these plants "exotics," meaning that they come from places far away. Many find their ways into local plant communities, impacting them to a greater or lesser degree. Some become invasive, crowding out native species and taking over large natural areas. We now consider many exotic plants to be weeds—dandelions, purslane, burdock, plantain, thistles, stinging nettles, and bittersweet, among many others, come from abroad.

But not all exotic plants are a problem. Go out on a summer's day to pick a bouquet of wildflowers, and you will likely come home with an assortment of exotics—buttercups, red clover, chickory, butter-and-eggs, Queen Anne's lace, tansy and, of course, daisies. None of these lovely plants were here before the European invasion. However, it is true that exotic plants as widespread as daisies and buttercups may have displaced native species. There may have been a very different ensemble of wildflowers on the coast of Maine before the advent of Europeans. I wonder, what flowers did the native Penobscot people gather for bouquets to please their sweethearts and decorate their homes?Summer

Summer

Baby Birds

There is a group of birds of the South Pacific islands and Australia called megapodes that literally do not have babies. Their eggs hatch into fully formed adults, ready to fly and feed themselves. The parents do not incubate the eggs. Rather, they build large mounds of vegetation covered with a layer of sand—essentially big compost piles. The mother lays her eggs, which are large and more than half yolk, in the compost pile. The heat produced by decomposition keeps the eggs warm. In about seven weeks the young birds hatch, dig their way out of the compost pile, and start their adult lives on the spot with no parents in sight.

Photo by Joan Handel

In North America, all birds have young that are dependent to some degree on their parents for care and feeding. Across the spectrum of bird species there are various degrees of development and dependency in baby birds. At one end of the spectrum are birds that hatch with their eyes open, covered with warm down, and able to walk almost immediately, like baby chicks or ducklings. At the other end of the spectrum are birds that hatch with their eyes sealed shut, buck-naked, and able only to lift their heads, open their yellow-lined beaks, and chirp loudly for food. If they are to survive, their parents must keep them warm and dry and feed them almost constantly.

Birds that hatch ready to leave the nest are called precocial, from the same Latin root as precocious. They hatch relatively mature and mobile, with downy feathers, open eyes, and good coordination. Most precocial chicks are not able to fully regulate their body temperature, and need their parents to brood them until their flight feathers grow in. There are variations in the condition at hatching of precocial birds. Ducklings and shorebird hatchlings leave the nest under the protection of their parents within a day or two and are immediately able to emulate their parents' example in finding food. Young quails and turkeys follow their parents from the nest but need the parents to show them how to find food. Other hatchling marsh and water birds such as rails and grebes leave the nest with their parents and are fed by them.

Birds that hatch completely dependent on their parents are called altricial, from the Latin for "needing nourishment." All songbirds, as well as perching birds such as crows and woodpeckers, are altricial. They hatch naked with their eyes sealed shut, totally dependent on their parents both for food and for shelter from heat and cold. Some larger birds, like owls, hawks, egrets, and herons, are called semi-altricial. Like their altricial cousins they are uncoordinated and helpless when they hatch, but they have developed a bit further inside the egg. Owls come into the world clothed in downy feathers. Hawks, egrets, and herons hatch with downy feathers and open eyes.

In general, precocial birds lay larger eggs with big yolks that are better stocked with protein than the eggs of altricial birds. This means the female must have abundant food resources before laying her eggs in order to provide them with sufficient protein. Precocial birds must incubate their eggs longer, usually three to four weeks, since more of the development of the chick happens inside the egg. Once hatched, however, precocial chicks are less vulnerable to predation, and even if predators take some of the young, others are likely to escape. The parental energy spent on feeding precocial babies is minimal, and usually only the mother is involved with their care.

On the other hand, altricial birds lay smaller eggs with smaller yolks, making it possible for the female to lay eggs in the absence of abundant food resources. Incubation is usually short—11 to 14 days. After the chicks hatch, the parents need to expend most of their energy feeding their babies throughout the daylight hours and keeping them warm and dry day and night. Altricial babies grow very fast. They soon open their eyes, sprout down and then flight feathers, and practice flapping. While the babies are in the nest, they are very vulnerable to predation, and a predator that finds the nest is likely to devour the entire clutch. Feeding the chicks, keeping them warm, and defending the nest usually require the efforts of both parents.

Altricial young fledge, or leave the nest, after about two weeks. In general, the parents (or the father, if the mother is starting another brood) continue to feed the young outside the nest for a while longer. You can sometimes observe young birds the same size as their parents, but often with the remnants of a yellow lining in their beaks and bits of downy fluff sticking out from their flight feathers begging a harassed parent for food. Young birds at this stage should be left alone by well-meaning humans. They may not yet be good fliers, but their parents are nearby watching over them.

Some birds lay all their eggs before starting to incubate them. In this case, all the babies will hatch together, or synchronously. In precocial species, hatching is synchronous so that all the chicks will be able to leave the nest at the same time. Many altricial species begin incubating as soon as their first egg is laid. Incubation continues as the mother lays subsequent eggs. In this case the babies will hatch one at a time, or asynchronously. Since the hatchlings will differ in age, the first will be larger and stronger than its nestmates and able to outcompete them for parental attention and food. This helps to ensure that in years when the food supply is poor at least one of the young is likely to survive, while in years of abundant food, the entire clutch may survive.

It is a dangerous world out there for birds. Only about ten to twenty percent of baby birds reach adulthood. Most fall victim to their own nestmates, to predators, to disease, to bad weather, and to accidents. But this is the season of hope. There are thousands of baby birds hatching in the late spring and summer, and some of them will make it through next winter and return to our forests, coasts, lawns, and feeders next year.

Red Tides and Phytoplankton

One of the pleasures of summer on Isle au Haut is digging clams and harvesting mussels. It is satisfying to trudge along the shore to the clam flat with clam forks and rollers and work up a sweat emulating our hunter-gatherer ancestors. We dig our dinner out of the mud, then rake up a batch of mussels as we wend our way home. But before we go out on an expedition, we check the Department of Marine Resources website for red tide closures. There have been a lot of them in recent years. A red tide is more accurately known as a harmful algal bloom or HAB, since it is neither red, nor connected in any way to the tides. A HAB is the result of a bloom of particular species of single-celled marine algae called phytoplankton.

Phytoplankton are microscopic, free-floating algae that live in the upper sunlit layers of both salt and fresh water. There are more than 5,000 species of phytoplankton. Like all plants, they harness the sun's energy, photosynthesizing to create their own food, and making oxygen as a byproduct. Phytoplankton produce more than half of the oxygen we breathe. Whoever called rainforests "the lungs of the earth" forgot the numberless, single-celled phytoplankton, the vast majority of which live in the ocean.

The word phytoplankton comes from the Greek "phyto" meaning plant, and "plankton" meaning wanderer. (Our word "planet" comes from the same root, since the planets appear to wander the night sky.) Phytoplankton float near the surface of the water carried by currents and stirred by winds and waves. Though many species have tiny appendages that they use to move small distances, in the greater scheme of things they go wherever the water takes them. Along with them go all the tiny organisms called zooplankton on which larger organisms feed.

Phytoplankton depend for survival on sunlight and on upwellings of minerals from the ocean bottom. In areas where such upwellings occur, phytoplankton can reproduce exponentially, creating billions of organisms over huge ocean areas. The Gulf of Maine is one such area, an almost self-contained basin of cold water protected by an underwater ridge that deflects the warm, northwestward-flowing Gulf Stream. Frigid, nutrient-rich water from Labrador is sucked into the Gulf of Maine through a deep channel on its northeastern end, stirring the waters and enhancing the habitat for phytoplankton. Abundant, cold-water phytoplankton is the foundation of the Gulf of Maine's rich aquatic ecosystems. Every year in the spring, triggered by lengthening daylight, there is a huge bloom of phytoplankton. There is also a smaller bloom in the fall.

Alarmingly, because of ocean warming, the spring phytoplankton bloom in 2012 was exceptionally early, and failed to provide nourishment for other species that depend on the timely appearance of phytoplankton. Then, in the warmest water ever recorded in the Gulf of Maine, the 2013 spring phytoplankton bloom failed altogether. This meant insufficient food for the tiny zooplankton, which share the sunlit ocean surface with the phytoplankton. In the inexorable way that food webs work, insufficient zooplankton meant insufficient food for the small fish that eat zooplankton, and finally insufficient food for larger species of fish, marine mammals and marine birds.

Though one needs a microscope to see individual phytoplankton, scientists also study them using satellites. Because the presence of phytoplankton changes the color of the ocean as seen from above, the location and composition of masses of plankton can be determined by analysis of color photographs taken from space.

The organisms we call red tides are particular toxic species of phytoplankton. The most dangerous phytoplankton in the Gulf of Maine is called *Alexandrium*. It contains a poison called saxitoxin that helps it to avoid being eaten by zooplankton. Ingesting large quantities of saxitoxin causes a disease called Paralytic Shellfish Poisoning, PSP, which can be fatal to humans.

How do humans get PSP from eating clams and mussels? Clams and mussels (and many other marine animals) are filter feeders. This means they suck seawater into their bodies, filter out the food they need, and squirt the water out again. When there is a lot of *Alexandrium* in the water, clams, mussels, and other filter feeders ingest it and digest it. The toxin remains in the animals' bodies and is concentrated there. If we eat clams or mussels that are full of saxitoxin we get sick or die, depending on the concentration of toxins and the amount we eat. Symptoms of PSP include numbness and tingling of the face, arms and legs, then headache, dizziness, nausea and muscular incoordination. Severe poisoning causes muscle paralysis and respiratory failure. There is no treatment for PSP except ventilator support in a hospital.

We are fortunate that the State of Maine has two programs that help to identify and locate harmful algal blooms. We have the Volunteer Phytoplankton Monitoring Program, which is run by the University of Maine Cooperative Extension, and the Department of Marine Resources Marine Biotoxin Monitoring Program. These programs work together to protect us from HABs. Community members and students up and down the coast volunteer to collect seawater and study it under microscopes, looking for *Alexandrium* and other toxic phytoplankton. They notify DMR of their findings. DMR scientists collect clams, mussels, and other shellfish weekly in many locations along the coast, with special attention to areas indicated by the volunteer monitors. DMR then analyzes the shellfish tissues for toxicity. Interestingly, in the summer of 2013, probably because of the failure of the spring phytoplankton bloom, red tides were much less of a problem than marine biologists had forecast based on data other than water temperature.

We have a lot to be thankful for. We should thank the scientists, volunteers, and officials who keep us safe from the poisons produced by a few species of phytoplankton. We should also thank the billions of phytoplankton from the deep past to the present, whose presence has been crucial for the development and perpetuation of life on our planet. It was phytoplankton that contributed the first oxygen to our atmosphere more than 500 million years ago, making it possible for life to emerge from the sea. It is still phytoplankton that keeps us supplied with much of the oxygen we breathe. And it is phytoplankton that feeds the animals that populate our oceans. As the planet warms and our oceans change, let's hope that the Gulf of Maine will still be able to sustain blooms of phytoplankton—even though these blooms can contain dangerous poisons. A clam dinner isn't much to sacrifice for all the benefits phytoplankton provide.

Gulls

(Larus argentatus, Larus marinus, Leucophaeus atricilla)

Every morning the first living thing I see when I open my eyes is a gull flying by the bedroom window. There are two common species on Isle au Haut, the herring gull, and the great black-backed gull. It is easy to tell them apart. The great black-backed gull is the world's largest gull, with black wings and a wingspan of 65 inches. The herring gull, our most common gull, has gray wings and a wingspan of 58 inches. A third species, the laughing gull, is much less common in mid-coast Maine. It is the smallest of our three gulls, with a black head and a cackling call. These three species exhibit similar behaviors and coexist along our shores, patrolling the coast, calling raucously to each other, harassing other birds, and generally making their presence known.

Photo by Joan Handel

All three species of Maine coastal gulls were almost wiped out from much of their range in the 1800s. They were hunted for the millinery trade and their eggs were collected for food. But they are now protected and have rebounded with a vengeance. In many places gulls are considered pests, flocking to feed in garbage dumps and attacking other birds and their eggs. In some places, they have earned the epithet "rats with wings." In the present day, herring gulls are expanding their range southward along the Atlantic coast, where they are displacing laughing gulls. However, in our area, great black-backed gulls are increasing and displacing herring gulls.

The abundance of gulls in a variety of places has caused controversy about gull control. Gulls living near airports create safety hazards because of potential collisions with planes. Inland, gulls can cause crop damage. In coastal areas, gulls share nesting islands where other less abundant seabirds such as terns, cormorants, razorbills, and guillemots are also raising young. Gulls prey on the eggs and chicks of their neighbors. This has created disputes between animal rights activists and conservationists about gull control on nesting islands. In general, conservation organizations such as the Audubon Society, the National Park Service, and state wildlife agencies support at least limited gull control measures. These measures, which require federal and state permits, include poisons, frightening devices, trapping, shooting, nest removal, and interference with or sterilization of gull eggs. Humans, with their garbage dumps and huge agricultural fields, have been a primary cause of gull population increase. Now we find ourselves in the position of having to artificially and forcefully decrease their numbers.

On Isle au Haut gulls are in their ideal coastal habitat. They inhabit the shoreland and the sea, hunting the mudflats and the rocky intertidal, fishing in open water, resting on ledges, beaches, and rocky outcroppings. They are omnivores, with a diet including crabs, mussels, sea urchins, squid, small fish, insects, carrion, and other birds and their eggs. They aggressively steal food from other birds (or from people on picnics). They pick food from the shore and pluck it from the surface of the water. They also dip under the water and plunge-dive for fish. It is fun to watch gulls fly up and drop mussels onto rocks to crack them open. Anywhere you walk on the rocky shore you will find crab and sea urchin shells on high places where gulls have brought them to feed in safety.

Gulls can drink both fresh and salt water. Like all true seabirds they have salt glands above their eyes with ducts that lead into the nasal cavities. These glands concentrate salt from the blood, and excrete it through their nostrils. This adaptation allows sea birds to drink salt water.

We do not observe gulls' breeding behavior because they nest in colonies on remote islands and shores. Gulls are monogamous, and mate for life. They have elaborate courtship rituals. A pair of gulls shares all parenting responsibilities. They make a scrape nest lined with grass and feathers. The parents share incubation of their three eggs and feed the chicks near the nest for two months. They continue to care for their young until the chicks are six months old, even after they have learned to fly.

Young gulls take three or four years to reach maturity. All those brown gulls you might have noticed are juvenile herring or black-backed gulls, not different species. In their first winter young gulls are dark brown and speckled. With each yearly molt their plumage becomes lighter, and the beak and legs change color, until at last they are beautiful black, grey and white adults. Mature great black-backed and herring gulls have pink legs and yellow beaks, while laughing gulls develop reddish-black legs and red beaks.

If I had to choose one type of bird that characterizes the Maine coast, it would be the seagull. They are here year round, though some move southward in the winter. Their strident cries, their beautiful flight, their large size, and their sheer abundance make them an emblem of our shores. It is hard to imagine what life here would be like without our gulls. Quieter and more refined, perhaps, but without the wild edge that constantly reminds us that we share this place with other creatures.

Bird Nests

A nest is not a bird's home in the sense that our houses are our homes. A nest is the place where a bird lays and incubates eggs and raises its young until they are ready to fledge. You could think of it as a cradle. Most nests are abandoned after one use, though large birds like raptors and herons often use the same nest year after year, adding new material each year. Some nests are huge. The largest bald eagle nest on record was almost ten feet wide and twenty feet deep. At the other end of the scale, a ruby-throated hummingbird's nest is the size of a walnut.

Not all birds construct their nests. Some birds, such as brown-headed cowbirds, are nest parasites. They avoid the work of parenting by laying their eggs in the nests of other birds. Some birds, such as black guillemots, nest in crevices on rocky shores. Some, such as screech owls, use holes in trees. Some seabirds, such as murres, lay eggs on rock ledges on cliffs facing the sea. Their eggs are very pointy on one end, so that they will roll in a tight circle if disturbed, preventing them from rolling off the cliff.

Birds that construct their nests make many different types. There are scrapes, platforms, burrows, tree cavities, cups, saucers, pendant nests, and spherical nests. Scrapes, which are simply shallow depressions in sand, soil, or vegetation, are the most vulnerable nests, because they are on the ground, exposed to weather and predators. Ground-dwelling birds such as turkeys, grouse, and quail, make scrape nests. Many of our common coastal birds including most sandpipers, plovers, sea ducks, and terns, are scrape nesters. The parent birds and the eggs of scrape nesters are often cryptically colored to camouflage them in the nest. Most of these scrape nesters have precocial young, which means their chicks hatch, like baby chickens, open-eyed and downy, ready to leave the nest under the care of their mother. They can run after her as soon as they are dry and fluffy. Scrape nests are used almost exclusively for incubation.

Hawks, eagles, ospreys, and herons make platform nests. These structures, constructed from sticks, are placed high in trees or sometimes on human-made structures like bridges, spindles, and buoys. The large size of platform nests helps to ensure that the young, which will be adult-sized when they fledge, will not fall off the increasingly crowded nest during their growth. Platform nests are used for multiple years and refurbished each year during the mating season. The parent birds bring new sticks and new lining material to the nest as a part of their courtship ritual. This reconstruction provides a clean surface on which to incubate and raise this year's young.

Puffins and storm petrels nest in rock crevices or in deep burrows, which they construct in the soil. The burrows and crevices provide protection from the elements and from predators. Many birds nest in tree cavities, either excavating the cavities themselves, like woodpeckers, or using natural or previously used cavities. People often entice cavity nesters such as chickadees, wrens, and bluebirds to their yards by putting up nest boxes.

When we think of bird nests most of us conjure up images of the woven nests of songbirds. The variety in shape, size, materials, and construction of songbird nests is one of the marvels of nature. There are cup nests, saucer nests, spherical nests, pendant nests, and domed nests. Each species of bird knows instinctively how to build its nest, though individuals get better with practice. Despite their instinctual programming, birds must be inventive in finding and using local materials. Usually the female of the species does the actual nest construction, though there are many exceptions to this generalization. The male, even if he does not assist with construction, often helps to choose the nest site, brings nesting materials to his mate, or shares incubation after the eggs are laid. In a few species, such as the house wren, the male does all the work. He builds several different nests, and his mate chooses the one she likes best.

Birds use their beaks to carry and weave materials, and often shape the nest with their bodies, turning round and round to create a perfect fit. There are several phases of nest building. First the bird establishes a foundation, a solid base or attachment to a tree branch. Then she weaves or otherwise constructs the walls or dome that will protect her eggs. Finally she lines the nest with soft materials such as plant down, grasses, moss, or feathers. Building a nest may take many days or only a day or two, depending on the complexity and intricacy of the job. A Baltimore oriole takes up to two weeks to finish her intricately woven pendant nest, while a robin builds her more slapdash mud nest in a couple of days. Many songbirds raise two or three broods of chicks in the course of a summer, and most build a new nest for each new brood. This helps avoid the growth of nest parasites and bacteria, while also deterring discovery of the nest by local predators.

One of my dreams in life is to find a ruby-throated hummingbird's nest. When I was a girl summering on a farm in Vermont, I learned that hummingbirds often nest in old apple trees on lichen-covered, horizontal branches. I had seen a photograph of a tiny, perfect nest woven from spider silk, bud scales, and lichen, lined with plant down. In the picture, the nest looked like a knot on a grizzled branch, practically invisible and yet a marvel of construction. I spent hours frequenting an old orchard near the farm, watching for hummingbirds. I figured if I saw one flying in the same direction over and over, that would guide me towards her nest. I never did find a nest, then or since, but the hummingbird nest remains as a kind of talisman in my mind, representing everything that is small, transient and beautiful.

Fireflies
(Lampyridae)

One Fourth of July about twenty years ago I was living alone in a farmhouse next to an apple orchard in Vermont. I didn't go to the local fireworks display—I have always dreaded the concussive booms. Instead, I sat behind the house in a folding chair overlooking the quiet meadow between me and the dark apple trees. I watched fireflies. There were thousands of them blinking everywhere, from the ground up to the treetops, merging in the sky with the stars. I'll never forget it, my personal Independence Day.

Though they are called fireflies or lightning bugs, fireflies are actually beetles. There are about 2,000 known species of fireflies worldwide, living on every continent except Antarctica. Fireflies are found in the tropics year round and in temperate environments in the summertime. They thrive in forests, meadows, and wetlands, preferring moist, warm habitats. Some fireflies are diurnal and do not emit light. The majority are nocturnal and must meet the challenges of finding others of their species in the dark. Some nocturnal insects, such as moths, rely on pheromones for communication. Others, such as crickets, rely on sound. Fireflies have evolved to communicate with each other using light.

The production of light by living organisms is called bioluminescence. Bioluminescence is also called "cold light," since almost 100% of the energy produced is emitted as light. Light production by human inventions is much less efficient. An incandescent bulb's energy output is 80% heat, and a fluorescent bulb's is 30% heat. Fireflies and other bioluminescent organisms are way ahead of us in energy efficiency.

Some terrestrial plants, fungi, and insects, as well as many marine fish, invertebrates, and phytoplankton are bioluminescent. The chemical reaction that makes the light is the same in all these organisms. Light-emitting cells store a chemical called luciferin, and an enzyme called luciferase. In the presence of oxygen and ATP, a molecule present in all cells that transforms chemical energy into other forms of energy, light is emitted. In adult fireflies, the process takes place in special organs in the lower abdomen.

The familiar flashing that enchants human observers on summer nights is the firefly's method of attracting a mate. A male flies through the darkness, emitting a series of flashes in a pattern that is unique to his species. The flash patterns of different firefly species differ in length, color, duration, pattern, number of flashes, and intervals between flashes. Males outnumber females by fifty to one. The females generally perch in vegetation or on the ground and watch for the flash pattern particular to their species. Females can afford to be very selective, often waiting for the brightest or fastest male. When she makes her choice, the female responds with a matching signal, calling the male down to mate. When he mates with her, he inserts a packet of nutritional protein along with his sperm.

There is a common group of firefly species known as "femmes fatales." The females imitate the flash patterns of a different species, inducing a male of that species to approach and (he thinks) mate with her. The femme fatale promptly seizes and eats him. When she does this, she incorporates his store of defensive chemicals as well as his nutritious proteins. A femme fatale can eat several hapless males in one night. But eventually, she flashes to attract a mate of her own species.

After mating, the female firefly lays her eggs in the soil. The eggs hatch three to four weeks later. All the firefly's life stages—eggs, larvae, pupae and adults—are bioluminescent. All are distasteful to predators, and often poisonous. The firefly's light alerts and deters predators, especially during the long and active larval stage. The newly hatched larvae conceal themselves during the day and forage during the night, shedding their larval skins periodically as they grow. The larvae are carnivorous, hunting primarily for snails, slugs, and earthworms that thrive in the moist, warm habitats preferred by fireflies. The larvae overwinter, pupate in the spring, and emerge as adults in the summer. Adult fireflies live only a few weeks.

Fireflies all over the world are in decline. During my childhood, a favorite evening activity for children was gathering fireflies in jars to watch them blink and to marvel at their otherworldly light. Nowadays I seldom see enough fireflies to make that lovely pastime possible. Scientists are not sure of all the reasons for fireflies' decline, but they believe that human encroachment on firefly habitat, toxic chemicals, and increased light pollution are the main culprits. All of these things can disrupt or prevent fireflies' mating success. If you want to encourage fireflies where you live, turn off your outside lights, allow logs and leaf litter in the moist corners of your yard to accumulate, don't use herbicides and pesticides, and let some of your grass grow tall. Perhaps your yard will twinkle with the ancient, magical light show of the fireflies.

Red Squirrels
(Sciurus vulgaris)

This year we have a bumper crop of red squirrels on Isle au Haut. Young, inexperienced animals are everywhere along the roadsides, foraging and exploring. Many are killed by cars, and their bodies are scattered on the blacktop, providing food for scavengers. Yesterday afternoon I was driving on the east side of the island and noted a dead squirrel ahead. Suddenly, right in front of my car, a broad winged hawk swooped out of the forest and scooped up the squirrel in its talons, its boldly striped tail flaring as it braked to make its grab. It carried off the prize, flapping hard to gain altitude. I had to brake, too. I'm still carrying that vivid picture of the hawk and the squirrel in my mind. I imagine that all the crows, ravens, hawks, owls and coyotes of Isle au Haut have their eyes on the roads this week, looking for a free meal.

Photo by Marnie Davis

Unlike gray squirrels, red squirrels are territorial animals. All of us have heard their loud, angry trills when we intrude on their space. Each red squirrel has its own private territory, which it defends fiercely from other squirrels. It builds a cozy nest lined with soft grass in a tree hole, inside a clump of witches' broom, or under logs. Our red squirrels depend on spruce trees for nesting sites and food—they eat spruce buds in the spring and store spruce cones for the winter. But they will eat lots of different foods, including nuts and seeds, baby snowshoe hares, bird eggs, and baby birds. They even eat mushrooms, which they hang up to dry in trees before storing them. Each squirrel stores a large cache of winter food, and frequents one or more nearby feeding spots where large piles of cone scales and other detritus called middens accumulate. The midden is an important part of a squirrel's territory, and some squirrel mothers build extra middens around their homesites to bequeath to their young.

Squirrels breed in late February or early March. Each female is fertile for only one busy day, when several males compete to mate with her. Her litter of four or five hairless, blind young is born in the nest five weeks later. The mother nurses her babies for about eight weeks, during which time they grow their fur, open their eyes, and begin to explore the area around the nest. Then the mother either moves her young to a nest at the edge of her territory or establishes a new territory for herself, abruptly weans her babies, and excludes them from her territory. That is what's happening right now on Isle au Haut. Suddenly, the little squirrels are on their own. Before winter comes each one will have to learn to fend for itself, establish a territory, make a nest, and build a midden. It is not surprising that only about 20 percent of the new squirrels survive their first year.

All the dead squirrels on the roads this week are a reminder that dispersal of young mammals is a dangerous, deadly process. The immature squirrels who innocently scamper about on the roadsides and nibble on tidbits of food have just been rejected by their mothers. They are learning their first, hard lessons about self-sufficiency, pitting their inexperience against cars, hawks, and other predators. Most of them will not pass the test.

Deer Ticks and Lyme Disease
(*Ixodes scapularis* and *Lyme borreliosis*)

A new activity for many people during the summer on Isle au Haut is the nightly tick check. Deer ticks are abundant on the island, and Lyme disease is a constant worry from April through November. Gone are the days of wandering heedlessly in fields of tall grass or bushwhacking through the huckleberries, or even lying on the lawn in the sunshine. But you may be able to reduce your risk of Lyme disease infection by understanding the extraordinary life cycle of the deer tick.

Ticks are arachnids, in the same class as spiders, scorpions, and mites. They are parasites that feed by attaching themselves to another animal and sucking its blood. A deer tick, after hatching from its egg, has three life stages: larva, nymph, and adult. It takes two years for the tick to go through the whole cycle. At each stage it needs a blood meal to progress to the next stage. This style of feeding makes the tick an ideal vector for disease. A vector is a carrier that transfers an infective agent from one host to another. The reservoir of Lyme disease infection is primarily the white-footed mouse and sometimes other small animals such as voles, songbirds, and shrews. A disease reservoir is the group of animals that carries the disease without becoming sick. These animals carry the Lyme bacteria around in their blood. If a tick at any stage of its life bites an infected mouse, the tick becomes infectious. So how and when are you liable to become infected with Lyme disease?

When a tick hatches from its egg into a larva it is disease free. The eggs hatch mostly in summer, and larvae are most active in July through September. They are tiny—about the size of a printed period—and non-infectious. A larval tick stays on the ground waiting for a small animal, most likely a mouse, to pass by. It grabs on, sucking blood until it is engorged. Whenever a tick drinks the blood of an infected host it can acquire Lyme disease bacteria from the host. At this point it becomes infectious to humans and other animals. After its first blood meal the larval tick drops off its host and uses the nutrition from its blood meal to transform into a nymph. If a nymph does not get a second blood meal by early autumn, it overwinters and becomes active again in spring when temperatures rise above 45 degrees.

The nymphal tick is the stage that is the most dangerous to humans. Studies show that up to 25% of mice carry Lyme disease, so we can deduce that we have approximately a one in four chance of infection if we are bitten by a nymph. The nymph is tan, about the size of a poppy seed, and difficult to notice before it becomes engorged with blood. Nymphs are active from May through July, but continue to be a threat through August. Like the larva, the nymph stays on the ground, waiting for a host animal to come by. This makes it most likely that we will be bitten by a nymphal tick if we lie in the grass or otherwise get close to the ground. It takes at least 36 hours for a tick to transmit Lyme disease, so it is important to check carefully and remove ticks promptly.

The engorged nymph drops off its host in late summer after a few days of feeding and transforms into an adult tick about the size of a sesame seed. It now has a 50% chance of being infected, and it needs one more blood meal in order to make eggs or sperm. Unlike the larvae and nymphs, adult ticks crawl upwards onto stalks of grass and other plants, sometimes as high as three feet, to await their last host. This gives them the name "deer tick" because their last host is likely to be a tall animal like a deer (or a human). There are not many mice three feet from the ground! Although adult ticks are more likely than nymphs to be infectious, they are easier to see and to remove before they infect us. Adult ticks are most active in the fall, as they look for their last host. If they don't find a host in the fall, they overwinter and try again in the spring. Adult ticks lay their eggs and die, and the cycle begins again.

About ten years ago, my partner and I lived in Central America for six months, working on service projects. We worried constantly about snakes, scorpions, fire ants, spiders, and myriad other menacing creatures. We were relieved to get home to the clean, safe coast of Maine, where he promptly got bitten by a tick and contracted Lyme disease. Go figure!

Bald Eagles, Fish, and Seabirds
(Haliaeetus leucocephalus)

The bald eagle has made a spectacular comeback on the coast of Maine since DDT was banned in 1972. Eagles, which were in danger of going extinct, are now a common sight on Isle au Haut and all along the coast of Maine. Our house sits high on a bluff above the ocean on the east side of Isle au Haut. When I am looking out at the view I can often tell when an eagle is passing by because all the seabirds resting on ledges or floating on the ocean fly up in alarm. If you review the literature on eagles you will learn that while they are opportunists when it comes to food, they are primarily fish eaters, adapted to snatch fish off the surface of the water with their talons in an unerring swoop. Not any more. At least on the coast of Maine.

Photo by Joan Handel

The decline of the bald eagle, which began when DDT came into common use after World War II, coincided with the decline of the ground fish in the Gulf of Maine. When eagles began to rebound in the 1970s and '80s there were fewer fish for them to catch, and they resourcefully learned to hunt seabirds. As eagles become more abundant their impact on seabirds grows. A few years ago I took my class of students from the Isle au Haut School to a local eagle nest up on a ridge in a big white pine to look for discarded bones underneath. Foraging around in the duff at the base of the tree, we found seabird bones, lots of them. That's what eagles are feeding their young.

Yesterday from our deck I watched an eagle hunt an unwary eider duck, who dived each time the eagle swooped down on him. The duck became increasingly exhausted, and finally the eagle prevailed. The eagle, down in the water with the duck, towed it to a nearby ledge, holding on with one taloned foot and rowing with its wings. It lugged the duck up onto the ledge, shook the water off its feathers, held the duck down with one foot, plucked it, and dug in for a meal, fending off scavenging crows and gulls as it feasted.

Eagles have another method of hunting seabirds. They fly out to remote nesting islands where colonies of seabirds such as gulls, eiders, cormorants, and terns raise their young. The eagles take eggs and young birds from the nests. One species that nests on the barren islands around Isle au Haut is the great cormorant, a larger cousin of the double-crested cormorant or shag. The only nesting sites in the United States for these elegant birds are here around Isle au Haut. And the eagles are wiping them out. John Drury of Vinalhaven, who counts great cormorant nests each year, reports a decline from 260 nests in 1992 to 80 nests in 2008. This decline is attributed solely to eagle predation.

What is a human to do? First we decimate eagle populations with DDT. Then we ban DDT and save the eagle while we're decimating fish populations. Now we're working on bringing back the fish while the eagles prey on seabird populations. And we're scrambling, with very limited resources for saving seabirds, to protect our seabird nesting islands from eagles that can't eat fish because we wiped out the fish. It's a complicated balance, and it is out of whack.

Zooplankton and the Intertidal Zone

Whenever I slip and slide down the rocks along the shore into a tidepool I am always amazed by the diversity of animal life in the intertidal zone. There are mussels, periwinkles, barnacles, sea stars, and limpets attached to the rocks. Tiny shrimplike crustaceans swim busily everywhere. Hermit crabs roam the tidepool bottoms, while green crabs and rock crabs scuttle for cover when I lift the seaweed or overturn a loose rock. None of these animals began their lives here. They all arrived after a journey in the marine zooplankton.

The word zooplankton comes from the Greek words for animal and wanderer. Marine zooplankton are animals of all shapes and sizes that drift in the surface water of the ocean. They range from tiny single-celled protozoans to huge lion's mane jellyfish, which can grow to 120 feet long. While many planktonic species can direct their movements to a greater or lesser degree, all zooplankton move wherever the currents and winds take them.

There are two varieties of zooplankton. One, called holoplankton, are animals that remain in the plankton for their entire lives. The holoplankton includes jellyfish, krill (the shrimplike creatures that are the primary food for baleen whales), and many other life forms. The other variety of zooplankton is called meroplankton, and includes animals that spend only a part of their lives in the plankton. Many animals whose adult forms are familiar to us, including crabs, lobsters, periwinkles, sea stars, sea urchins, marine worms, sea anemones, clams, mussels, barnacles, and most fish, begin their lives as eggs and larvae drifting in the plankton.

Most animals we see in the tidepools and clam flats of coastal Maine start out as tiny, free floating creatures that look very different from their parents. As they grow, feeding on phytoplankton (the plant version of plankton) or on each other, they change many times, eventually becoming miniature versions of adult organisms. At this point they settle to the bottom, seeking places to begin their adult lives. Only a tiny percentage of the billions of larval animals in the meroplankton ever become adults. The vast majority are eaten, die, or fail to find a suitable habitat when they make their move to the bottom.

There are various reproductive strategies for the marine animals that begin their lives in the plankton. Many, like mussels, clams, sea stars, sea urchins, and clam-worms, reproduce by free spawning. This means that the adults simply release their eggs and sperm into the water, where fertilization takes place randomly. This method requires that the adults have environmental triggers or chemical communication methods that induce them to release their eggs and sperm at the same time in the same area. Environmental triggers include water temperature, day length, time of day, and abundance of prey or predators. Animals that can move, like worms, sea stars, and sea urchins, may release pheromones that prompt them to gather in one place before spawning, increasing the chances of fertilization.

Other animals, such as periwinkles, lobsters, and crabs mate with each other, transferring sperm packets called spermatophores from male to female. The female periwinkle fertilizes her eggs and releases them in mucousy bundles into the water, where they float up to the surface and join the plankton, eventually hatching into larval snails and feeding on phytoplankton. Lobsters and crabs mate when the female has just shed and has a soft shell. The male deposits his sperm packet inside the female. When she is ready, she fertilizes her eggs internally, extrudes them, and carries them on her body—often for many months—until they hatch. As the eggs hatch, the tiny larvae leave their mother and rise to the surface, where they feed on smaller zooplankton. They shed their shells many times before achieving their adult form and settling to the bottom.

Barnacles, which are crustaceans like shrimp, lobsters, and crabs, are hermaph-rodites. Each animal has both male and female organs. But a barnacle does not fertil-ize itself. Therefore, it must solve the problem of how to mate with another barnacle while firmly attached to a rock. Barnacles accomplish this by having the longest penis, relative to body size, of any animal. It is as much as eight times as long as the body, long enough to stretch over to a neighboring barnacle to deposit a sperm packet. With barnacles, mate selection is all about proximity. A mated barnacle stores the sperm packet separately from the eggs, fertilizing the eggs when conditions are right. He/she then holds them inside the shell after they hatch until there is adequate food in the water. Then the larval barnacles are released and float away in the plankton.

The animals that you see when you go to a tidepool or a clam flat have parents that may have spawned far up or down the coast, depending on the local currents and winds. This ensures genetic mixing and fosters healthy populations. Each adult animal is one improbable survivor of billions of its species that never reached adulthood. Even the multitudes of adult barnacles and periwinkles, whose number seems to us to be legion, are the tip of the planktonic iceberg. Beyond the tidepools, beyond the clam flats, is a sea of life where whole ecologies exist beyond our wildest imaginings.

Ospreys
(Pandion haliaetus)

On Isle au Haut every year at the beginning of April we have a contest to guess the exact arrival date of the ospreys that nest on the spindle in the Isle au Haut Thorofare. A calendar is posted in the store and people write their names in the date squares, hoping to hit the exact day on which the first osprey will return. The winner gets a small prize and the satisfaction of having made an accurate prediction. It is a rite of spring here, and we all look forward to the new nesting season.

Photo by Marnie Davis

The osprey, or fishhawk, is a large raptor with a white breast and belly, black back and wings, a white head with a dark eyestripe, and a wingspan of four to five feet. It holds its wings somewhat crooked in flight. The osprey is easily distinguished from gulls by its smaller head, shorter tail, and five finger-like feathers at the wingtips. The female is slightly larger than the male, but it is hard to tell the difference unless you see them together. Unlike most species of birds, the osprey is found worldwide, living on every continent except Antarctica. Our Maine ospreys breed here and migrate to northern South America for the winter.

Ospreys feed almost exclusively on fish. They hover high above the water, looking down to spot their prey beneath the surface, and then plunge dive, feet first, to grasp fish in their talons. They have four talons, three in front and one behind, but can swivel one of the forward facing talons backwards when fishing. This adaptation, and the sharp bristles on the toe pads, make it easier for the osprey to hold onto its slippery prey. When an osprey snags a fish, it always carries it with the fish's head facing forward, making flight more aerodynamic.

Ospreys mate for life, separating for the winter and reuniting at the nest site in the spring. They nest in tall trees and on man-made structures such as telephone poles, bridges, and channel markers near fresh or salt water. Each pair returns to its nest year after year, renovating every spring by adding branches brought by the male and softer material for lining the nest cup brought by the female. The pair has a courtship period during which the male continually offers food to the female, brings her branches to refurbish the nest, and performs dramatic sky dances to impress her. Ospreys mate frequently for several weeks. The female lays two or three eggs over a week or so, beginning incubation as soon as the first egg is laid. The female incubates the eggs for five to six weeks. Throughout the breeding period, until the young are almost ready to fledge, the male brings all the food to the female and the young.

Young ospreys hatch sequentially, sometimes as much as five days apart. The first to hatch has a size and strength advantage over the others. In years when the fishing is good all the chicks may survive. In poorer years the firstborn is often the sole survivor. Though this adaptation may seem cruel, it makes survival of at least one of the young more likely. For the first six weeks, the father hunts and brings fish to the nest, and the female tears off little pieces to feed to the babies. After about four weeks, usually in early August, the young begin to stand at the edge of the nest and exercise their wings, getting ready for flight. At this stage, the mother starts to leave the nest to hunt, and both parents drop whole fish into the nest for the young. Finally, at about two months, the young ospreys fledge and begin to follow their parents around begging for food. They return to the nest at night to roost. The young start to fish on their own and soon leave on their fall migration, preceding their parents southwards.

In recent years, the osprey population has declined in eastern North America. This may be related to the increasing population of bald eagles along the coast, since eagles and ospreys compete for territory and food. On Isle au Haut we sometimes see an eagle harass an osprey, trying to make it drop its prey so that the eagle can abscond with it. When eagles and ospreys compete for nesting territory, the larger, stronger bird will usually win the day. But for now, ospreys dominate Isle au Haut Thorofare, raising their babies in the midst of the boat traffic, chirping angrily at passing fishermen and yachtsmen, and soaring majestically over the harbor all summer.

Blood Meals

Mosquitos, along with black flies, horseflies, and deerflies, are a major annoyance to humans and other warm-blooded animals from springtime through autumn in New England. Entomologists, the scientists who study insects, classify these critters in the order Diptera, or flies. Diptera means "two wings" in Latin. Flies have only one pair of wings, while bees, butterflies, dragonflies, beetles, grasshoppers, and other flying insects have two pairs.

Flies that bite have been bedeviling humans for a long time. Native Americans of this region used to travel every year at black fly season to summer encampments on Isle au Haut where they could enjoy clams, mussels, and lobsters without being seriously tormented by the swarms of insect pests on the mainland. They probably stayed all summer. But even on the island, the bugs can drive you crazy.

Black fly bites swell and burn, making me both unsightly and uncomfortable in the early summer. As the weather warms up I swim in Long Pond every day, and I am often dive-bombed by relentless horseflies. When I surface to look around and enjoy the view I find myself wildly swatting my head. Or I might take a leisurely evening stroll to a cove—only to be driven to a dead run to flee mosquitoes. Deerflies buzzing in crowds around my head are an annoyance I have grudgingly learned to tolerate when I walk in the woods. Why do all these critters have such a hankering for my blood?

Biting flies want blood for one reason: to get enough protein to manufacture eggs. Flies can't chew; they can only suck or lap up liquid foods. Most of the time—and for the males, all of the time—flies feed by sucking or lapping up nectar and moist substances of various sorts. But female biting flies have complicated piercing mouthparts. Each female mosquito has a grooved proboscis with saw-toothed, needlelike stylets that she can slip into your skin more painlessly than the most accomplished acupuncturist. Female deerflies, horseflies, and black flies all have scissorlike, slashing blades that cut into skin, causing blood to well up.

As they bite, mosquitoes and flies inject an anticoagulant to keep blood flowing. It is this irritant, not the puncture, that causes the redness, itching, and swelling that bother us after the biter is long gone. Many animals that get bitten have little power to repel the biter. Sometimes the maddening hum in my henhouse when I go in at dusk to shut the hens in for the night makes me wonder why my chickens don't need transfusions in the morning. On four-legged animals, a biting fly properly positioned out of reach of head or legs or swishing tail can settle in for a long drink of blood. You would think that a horsefly or mosquito could understand that she is unlikely to get a full meal from a crazed, swatting human, but evidently their persistence often pays off in the end.

Male mosquitoes die shortly after mating, but females can mate and bite more than once, creating several egg masses in a season. Revenge is one reason to splat the blood-filled mosquito on the bedroom wall the morning after. Another reason is that killing her may infinitesimally reduce the number of mosquitoes that will be whining in your ears a few weeks down the road.

Milkweed and Monarchs
(*Asclepias syriaca* and *Danaus plexippus*)

Like many gardeners I enjoy butterflies, and I like to plant flowers that attract them. Milkweed is one of these flowers. I nurture a stand of it by my front door. In late spring its strong shoots emerge from deep beneath the surface. Milkweed roots grow horizontally outwards from a central underground crown. Typically, one plant generates many stems growing close together. The result is often a dense patch that shades out other plants. In a garden setting, because of its late emergence and deep roots, milkweed is easy to combine with spring bulbs. In my garden, milkweed sprouts up just as daffodils and grape hyacinths are dying away.

Photo by Robert Abuza

Milkweed stalks grow tall by the summer solstice and soon produce clusters of fragrant pink flowers along the stems. The flowers are a magnet for many pollinators—especially bees and butterflies. Throughout the summer and early fall, monarch butterflies gather and float in loose groups around the milkweed patch. Their complex lives completely depend on milkweed, which is the sole food plant for monarch butterfly caterpillars. Other common colorful butterflies, including painted ladies, American ladies, red admirals, and several species of fritillaries, chase each other over the flowers. As the summer progresses, the flowers generate large, bristly seedpods packed with overlapping dark-brown seeds. Each seed is equipped with a silken parachute that unfolds as the pod dries and opens in the fall. The parachute carries its seed away on the breeze. At last, the skeletal stalks, with their empty seedpods, are left standing to face the oncoming winter.

Milkweed is a plant with many defenses against anything that might want to eat it. The leaves are covered with tiny hairs, which are hard for little critters to chew through. The white, sticky sap, which gives milkweed its common name, contains a latex that coagulates when exposed to air, and can glue the mouth of a small caterpillar closed. If these lines of defense fail, milkweed sap contains a strong poison called a cardenolide (from the Greek word kardia meaning "heart"), which dramatically affects blood pressure in all animals. Traditional herbalists use controlled doses of milkweed to treat congestive heart failure and atrial fibrillation. In fact, the scientific name of the milkweed family is Asclepias, for the Greek god of medicine. You might expect that milkweed, with its powerful defenses, would be able to fend off insects looking for food. But you would be wrong.

The process of evolution encourages diversity. Thus, a plant which is toxic to many organisms may become food and shelter for a few, the few that have evolved to overcome its defenses. Milkweed supports a fascinating community of insects that manage to tolerate its hairy leaves, sticky sap, and poisons. A number of species of insects use milkweed as a food plant. A few types of aphids suck its juices; a few beetles, caterpillars and fly larvae eat its leaves; a few bugs nibble its seeds; a few weevils bore into its stems; a few beetle larvae tunnel into its roots. Some insects that eat milkweed incorporate its poison into their bodies, thus appropriating the milkweed's defenses as their own. The monarch butterfly is one of those insects, and its fascinating life cycle is completely interwoven with the milkweed plants on which it feeds.

Most of us know that monarch butterflies migrate to central Mexico in the fall and spend the winter resting in traditional groves of fir trees in the mountains of the state of Michoacan. What you may not know is that the monarchs that migrate south in the fall are four generations removed from the monarchs that migrated north from Mexico the previous spring. The butterflies that make the long journey from North America to Mexico in the fall do not mature sexually until the following spring. They spend the winter months in Michoacán. They rest all winter, roosting in fir trees in the moist, cool climate of this mountainous region. The fir groves are warm enough to keep the monarchs from freezing, and cold and moist enough to allow them to survive without needing food. They enter a state called diapause, a kind of suspended animation, occasionally awakening and fluttering about, and then returning to their roost trees. These trees are completely festooned with millions of monarchs.

In March as the weather begins to warm, monarchs begin their northward journey, and attain sexual maturity. They travel several hundred miles north, somewhere near the Texas border. Their journey coincides with the spring emergence of milkweed plants. This is the first generation of the summer. These adult monarchs mate, lay their eggs, and die. Monarch caterpillars eat only one thing—milkweed—and female monarchs lay all their eggs on milkweed plants. The eggs hatch and mature, becoming the second generation of monarchs. This generation travels farther north, as does the third generation. By the end of summer, monarchs' range covers most of North America. Finally, the fourth generation hatches, pupates, and makes the long journey south to Mexico.

Monarchs usually reach Maine in late June, in their second generation. Both males and females gather around stands of milkweed, the males looking for mates, and the females looking for a place to lay eggs. The female lays her eggs one at a time on the undersides of milkweed leaves. Milkweed is hairy, sticky and poisonous, but monarch caterpillars are well equipped. A baby caterpillar hatches, eats its egg case, and then cuts a leaf vein upstream from its feeding area so that it can eat without sticky sap flowing into its mouth. It incorporates milkweed toxin into its body, making itself (and the butterfly into which it develops) poisonous to birds and other predators. The monarch caterpillar's distinctive yellow, black, and white stripes, and the butterfly's bright orange and black coloration, are a warning for birds: I am poisonous and distasteful!

Less than two weeks after hatching, a monarch caterpillar, having eaten nothing but milkweed, weighs two thousand times what it weighed on the day it hatched. During that milkweed banquet the caterpillar sheds (and eats) its skin five times. Each new phase is called an "instar." At last, having lost interest in eating, the fifth instar caterpillar wanders off to a twig or leaf to hang upside down, attaching itself with a button of silk, hanging in a J-shape as it prepares for transformation. It sheds its caterpillar skin for the last time and changes into a chrysalis, a jewel-like pale green case marked with black lines and gold dots.

Inside the chrysalis, enzymes are released that dissolve the former caterpillar into a rich, living broth. Within that broth are small groups of cells called "imaginal discs." Each disc is like a tiny embryo for a part of the developing butterfly. There are imaginal discs for each wing, leg, antenna, and organ of the butterfly-to-be. In about ten days, the metamorphosis is complete. The chrysalis is now transparent, and the dark orange and black striped wings are clearly visible inside. The adult monarch butterfly bursts the skin of the chrysalis, and flops down, hanging precariously onto the skin of the chrysalis with its new legs. Its abdomen is large and engorged with fluid, and its wings are tiny and wrinkled. The new butterfly pumps the fluid from its abdomen through the veins of its wings, expanding them. The butterfly must hang on until its wings are dry and rigid. It exercises its new wings, folding and unfolding them repeatedly, testing their strength until at last it launches itself into the air for the first time. The monarch in flight is a strong and graceful creature.

If the hatching butterfly is a fourth generation animal, it starts its long journey south. On the way it will depend on the nectar from fall wildflowers and garden flowers for the energy it needs to complete its long, dangerous flight south. Only a few of those that hatch—especially from as far north as Maine—make it all the way to Mexico. Recent scientific work shows that monarchs navigate on their southward journey both by orienting themselves to the position of the sun and by using an internal magnetic compass that orients them to the earth's magnetic field. They unerringly arrive at the same groves of fir trees in Michoacán each year.

The miracle of monarch butterfly migration is one of the wonders of nature in North America. Every fall our fishermen report streams of monarchs heading south over the water. Once I was walking with a friend in late August and we came upon a spreading ash tree festooned with hundreds of resting monarchs hanging with folded wings from the branches. But the monarch migration is a fragile thing. Monarch populations are declining. Milkweed is less common in the Midwest that it used to be. Climate change threatens migrating monarchs with unstable weather, rising temperatures, fiercer storms, and drought. The monarchs flying along our coast, floating over our meadows, and feeding on our fall flowers are precious reminders of the complexity of natural processes. I hope that we humans will work to protect the resources the monarchs need to continue their migratory journeys into the future.

The Plight of Monarch Butterflies in 2013

(Danaus plexippus)

There is a large stand of milkweed right by our front door that I have encouraged and enjoyed for many years. I love milkweed's big oval leaves, beautiful fragrant flowers, and spiny seedpods. Even more, I love the monarch butterflies that gather around my milkweed to partake of its nectar and to lay their eggs on its leaves. I love the big, black, white, and yellow striped monarch caterpillars that methodically munch away the leaves. I love the green and gold-flecked chrysalises that hang on our shingles and window frames.

Photo By Kathie Fiveash

But this year is different. Every time I step out the front door I am confronted with the absence of monarchs. Usually monarchs begin to arrive on Isle au Haut in late June, and by August there are hundreds. This year, at the beginning of August, I have seen a total of perhaps twenty butterflies swooping and soaring gracefully about the yard. When I see one, my heart leaps up with hope, but the low numbers are ominous. I wonder if this could be the last summer for migratory monarchs. What has happened?

Monarch butterflies have an extraordinary life story. They overwinter as adults in traditional forested sites on mountain slopes in central Mexico. In mid-March, they leave these winter roosts and head north, synchronizing their journey with the spring appearance of milkweed, their essential host plant. The generation of monarchs that leaves Mexico reproduces and dies near the Texas border. They lay their eggs on milkweed leaves, which provide food for their caterpillars. The caterpillars grow, transform into chrysalises, and metamorphose into butterflies. The new generation of butterflies continues north and reproduces. Monarchs fan out northwards, breeding as they go, over the entire North American continent to central Canada.

Each new generation of adult monarchs lives from two to four weeks until the emergence of the fourth generation, the great-great-grandchildren of the butterflies that began the northward journey from Mexico. This last generation of the summer postpones its reproductive development and migrates all the way back to Mexico. Here in Maine in the late summer and fall, we are host to that last generation, the adults who will make the miraculous flight of 3,000 miles or more. The southward migration usually begins in mid-August and continues until October. The butterflies that survive the migratory journey will roost for the winter in Mexico on the same trees their great-great-grandparents left seven or eight months before.

Insect populations are prone to fluctuations, but the decline of monarchs has been a general trend since the mid-nineties. The most important reasons are climate change and habitat loss, both in Mexico and in the United States. Climate change took an especially heavy toll this past year. The extreme heat of the spring of 2012, as well as the summer drought, caused low reproductive rates and low migratory survival for monarchs on both their northward and southward migrations. The population of adult butterflies wintering in Mexico in 2012-2013 was down by 80% from about 350 million to about 60 million butterflies. The area of trees covered with monarchs was less than 3 acres, compared with a yearly average of 17 acres.

This spring of 2013, cold wet weather slowed both the migration north and the development of the first generations of monarchs. As a result, monarchs are moving north very late and may not have time to complete four generations this summer, which will result in a very small southward migration this fall.

In the big picture over many years, habitat loss has been the most important factor in the decline of monarchs. During the 1990s, illegal logging operations in Mexico threatened the wintering grounds of the monarchs. But monarch tourism has become very important to the Mexican regions near the monarchs' winter roosts. Both local and national Mexican government action has curtailed illegal logging. This has greatly diminished habitat destruction on monarch wintering grounds. The critical problem for monarchs now is here in the United States. The amount of milkweed, the plant essential for monarch survival, is decreasing rapidly. Why?

Milkweed is a common plant along the edges of American corn and soybean fields. In the past ten years most large farms have started using Roundup Ready corn and soybean seeds. These seeds are genetically engineered to be immune to Roundup, the popular herbicide manufactured by Monsanto, the company that also supplies Roundup Ready seeds. As a result farmers are no longer tilling their corn and soybean fields to control weeds. Instead, they spray Roundup over their entire acreage, killing all plants except the Roundup Ready crops. This practice saves farmers a lot of money and labor. Milkweed has become a casualty of this practice.

The problem is exacerbated by the demand for corn to make ethanol. In the past farmers have been paid by the government to set aside land for wildlife, and have left other marginal lands unfarmed—lands totaling about 25 million acres that were ideal habitat for milkweed. Now there is incentive to farm every one of those acres. Throughout the Midwest, through which most migrating monarchs must pass, milkweed is becoming scarce. Without sufficient milkweed on which to lay their eggs, monarchs cannot successfully multiply.

Conservation groups such as Monarch Watch are now promoting a popular movement to cultivate milkweed across America. Roadsides are an excellent habitat for milkweed, and citizens can urge State and Federal Highway Departments to plant milkweed and other wildflowers instead of grass along our highways. Our Interstate Highway System could become a critical pathway for monarch butterfly migration. And all of us can plant milkweed in our gardens and fields. Monarch Watch (www.monarchwatch.org) can advise interested citizens how to participate in the effort to restore milkweed and save the migrating monarchs.

We must act quickly. We may already be too late. There is a critical mass, and no one knows exactly what that is, below which the monarchs face catastrophe. It may be that the few butterflies we are seeing this summer are the last migrating monarchs we will ever see. It makes me terribly sad and fearful to write this. By this time of the summer, my milkweed plants are usually tattered, half eaten away by monarch caterpillars. This year, they are pristine. The flowers with their heavenly fragrance are fading and the seedpods are beginning to form. But the legions of monarchs that usually grace my garden are missing.

Longfin Squid
(Doryteuthis pealeii)

Every night for the past six weeks the Isle au Haut Town Dock has been a gathering place for anyone interested in seeing or catching squid. There are multitudes of squid. They are long, slender, graceful, swift animals, beautifully marked with red patterns. Their presence is a mysterious phenomenon—no one knows why they come, how long they'll stay, or why they leave. Islanders remember another summer many years ago when squid swarmed into our harbor as they did this summer. Their reappearance after so long has marked this season with a special quality, as our Thorofare came alive in an unexpected way.

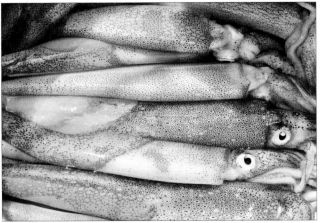

Photo by Marnie Davis

Squid are attracted to the bright lights that burn all night at the dock. People arrive after dark to fish with hooks, squid jigs, buckets and coolers. When squid are swarming, you can catch them by simply throwing out a hook and snagging one. Some people come just to peer into the water and marvel at the myriad beautiful creatures schooling thickly together under the lights.

Atlantic longfin squid are mollusks, related to snails and clams. They belong to a large class called cephalopods, which includes squids, octopi, and nautiluses. Squid are considered by scientists to be the most intelligent invertebrates. They demonstrate advanced spatial learning, navigational abilities, and hunting behaviors. Males are larger than females, reaching about 18 inches, while females grow to about a foot long.

Squids do not swim headfirst; rather, they propel themselves backwards through the water by jet propulsion. The head of the squid includes eight arms and two long tentacles, all equipped with suckers used for catching and holding prey. The arms and tentacles encircle a hard beak for tearing up food and a raspy tonguelike organ called a radula that draws food into the body cavity. Behind the arms and tentacles are two large, human-like eyes that provide them with exceptionally good vision. When you observe squid in the water, the eyes are prominent and seem to glow in the dark.

Behind the head is the mantle, a tubular body wall that encloses the viscera. Along the sides of the mantle are two long triangular fins for steering. The mantle encircles the head rather like a turtleneck. The space between the mantle and the head serves as a water intake. The squid can suck water into the mantle and then squirt it forcibly out the siphon, a tube that protrudes beyond the edge of the mantle along the side of the head. The siphon can be precisely aimed to allow the squid to jet through the water, moving with extraordinary speed and agility. Squid are the fastest invertebrate swimmers on earth. Their speed combined with their excellent vision make them formidable predators on fish, crustaceans, and smaller squid. At the same time, their abundance and schooling habit make them important prey for many fish, diving birds, and marine mammals. Standing on the Isle au Haut Town Landing, we watched seals and large mackerel hunting them. The squid reacted instantly, scattering in all directions, seeming to disappear in a flash. When squid are caught by predators or fishermen, they squirt a dark, inky substance that muddies the water, giving them a last chance at escape.

A squid's skin is covered with tiny, pigmented organs called chromatophores. These organs can expand and contract, giving the squid an intricate, speckled pattern over its body. Longfin squid are primarily dappled red, but can become pale green, or even black. A squid changes color to camouflage itself or to signal its mood or intention to other squid.

Longfin squid range along the Atlantic continental shelf from Newfoundland to Venezuela. They are social animals, gathering in huge schools. They winter in deep waters offshore where the temperature is stable. They migrate back to the coast as the ocean warms in the spring. Squid mate during this migratory journey, with a second, smaller mating period in the fall. Males aggressively court females, and deposit sperm packets under the females' mantles. A female may mate multiple times. When they reach shallow water, the females gather in large groups to extrude their eggs. They hold the gelatinous egg masses in their arms while fertilizing them with the stored sperm from several males. They deposit the eggs in huge communal clusters called sea mops, which are attached to rocks or seaweeds. In recent weeks, Isle au Haut lobstermen have been hauling up sea mops in their traps.

Adult squid only live to spawn once and will die before the migration back to their winter range. The squid eggs hatch and the larvae float up into the plankton, where they go through two juvenile stages. In juvenile stage two, they migrate to their winter range. They mature the following summer or during their second summer, depending on when they hatched.

Schools of squid spend summer days near the sea bottom and come to the surface at night to hunt. They are attracted to lights and prefer warm water, which may be what brought them to our Town Landing this summer. Because squid are particularly sensitive to ocean temperatures, scientists predict that populations may move farther north as the planet warms.

There is much that is not known about longfin squid, but one aspect of their biology has been thoroughly studied. The squid, because of its need for quick reflexes, rapid acceleration, and fast changes in direction, has evolved unusual nerve fibers that stimulate the muscles controlling jet propulsion. These nerves, which grow to 10 centimeters, are thicker and longer than any mammalian nerves. Neuroscientists interested in nerve function have found squid nerves to be invaluable tools for studying conduction of impulses and nerve physiology.

As August begins, the squid seem to be departing the waters around Isle au Haut. The last few nights, the fishing has tailed off, and the late-night groups of kids and teenagers and older fishermen straggle home early. But in the minds of the night watchers, the vision remains of the swarms of squid populating our familiar waters with their strange and mysterious lives.

American Eels
(Anguilla rostrata)

Every time I swim in Long Pond I think about American eels. There are a couple of reports every summer of swimmers being nipped by eels and I always worry a little bit, though I know that eels are active mostly from dusk to dawn, and I have never seen one outside a trap. I'm not at all squeamish about slimy creatures, but I draw the line at getting bitten, especially by an animal that may be three feet long at maturity.

The American eel is the only North American catadromous fish. This means it is born in the sea, migrates to fresh water to mature, and returns to the sea to spawn. The American eel spawns in the western Sargasso Sea, a huge area of clear, calm water in the middle of the North Atlantic Ocean surrounded by a gyre of ocean currents including the Gulf Stream. Mature American eels migrate to the Sargasso Sea from their huge freshwater range—lakes and rivers from northern South America all the way up the Atlantic coast to southern Greenland. Mature eels leave their freshwater homes in late summer, arriving in the Sargasso Sea in autumn. No one has ever witnessed their spawning, but it is known that each female releases one to four million buoyant eggs, which are fertilized in the water by sperm released by the males. All eels die after spawning, sinking to the ocean floor and leaving the new generation to fend for itself.

Baby eels hatch in February in the Sargasso Sea, which is home to Sargassum weed, a seaweed that floats in great rafts over its surface. Sargassum weed provides protection from predators for the newly hatched eels, as well as for other creatures like baby sea turtles. At this stage the baby eels are tiny transparent fish shaped like willow leaves. For about a year they join the plankton floating about in the Sargassum weed. While they grow they move slowly westward into the Gulf Stream, where they are carried north by the current. As they travel, they transform into a new stage called glass eels about 2 ½ inches long—still transparent, but with the characteristic eel shape. They are able to smell fresh water, and move shoreward towards the scent in the early spring. As they enter coastal areas they gain pigment, and are called elvers. At this stage of life they are very valuable to humans as a food delicacy. In Maine, licensed elver fishermen harvest them by the thousands as they move into our rivers. Elvers are sold in Asian markets to be raised to adulthood in aquaculture facilities. Most eventually become unagi sushi.

While some elvers stay in the sea or in brackish waters to mature, most move upstream slowly, growing into a new stage called the yellow eel. It may take ten to thirty years until they finally settle in lakes or rivers, often far inland. Eels populate the Rio Grande, the entire Mississippi River system, Lake Champlain, Lake Ontario, Long Pond on Isle au Haut, and any other body of fresh water connected to the ocean—in other words, a pond or stream near you! At this stage, yellow eels are sexually undifferentiated.

The American eel has a close cousin, the European eel. Though the two are different species, their behavior and life cycle are very similar. The European eel spawns farther east in the Sargasso Sea, and the young drift in the Gulf Stream longer than their American cousins, thereby travelling farther east. European elvers begin to gravitate to fresh water in the North Atlantic, eventually populating rivers and lakes in Iceland, Scandinavia, and Great Britain, and entering the Mediterranean Sea to travel up all its rivers as well as the rivers that drain into the Black Sea.

Eels are fierce carnivores, hunting insects, fish, clams, mussels, frogs, and carrion. They can swim backwards and forwards equally fast. Despite their small mouths, eels can eat large prey species by grasping onto them with their jaws and spinning an amazing ten to fourteen times per second, thus tearing off pieces of flesh. Eels feed mostly at night and probably locate their prey by smell.

Near the end of its life—anywhere from four to forty years—the yellow eel begins its migration back to the sea. During this migration, it transforms from a freshwater bottom-dweller to an ocean traveler. It attains sexual maturity and becomes dark with silvery undersides. In this final stage of its life, it is called a silver eel. Scientists believe that mature eels' gender is determined not by genetics, but by environmental conditions such as salinity, population density, and food quality and availability. Migrating eels put on fat reserves before their long sea journey. They do not feed at all during migration and spawning. Their eyes become larger and more sensitive for deep-water vision, and their buoyancy increases. In the fall, they end their journey where it began in the Sargasso Sea. There they spawn and die.

Populations of American eels are decreasing dramatically because of elver fishing and because of the dams and hydropower facilities eels meet on their upstream and downstream migrations. Concern about overfishing has prompted Delaware, Maryland, Massachusetts, New Hampshire, Rhode Island and Virginia to prohibit elver fishing. So perhaps I should be grateful that there are still eels in Long Pond who, though they might nip me in the process, have a good chance to get back to the Sargasso Sea.

$\mathcal{S}$piderwebs

On misty mornings in mid to late summer I often awaken to a lawn studded with saucer-shaped spider webs. These delicate structures, like gauzy hankies strewn on the grass, become invisible as the dew dries. Walking in summer fields, I sometimes come across the orb web, up to two feet in diameter, of a black and yellow argiope spider, commonly known as a garden spider. She hangs head downward at the web's center on a zipper-like structure of thickly woven silk, waiting to capture an unwary insect in her trap. In the corners of my house, where spiders keep the rest of the insect world at bay, silken egg cases protect the next generation of spiders from harm. One late summer day on our deck I watched newly hatched baby spiderlings launch into the world, like Charlotte's children did, spinning out lines of silk that were caught by the wind, flying away. The spiderlings disappeared into the sky, headed into the future on gossamer lifelines.

Photo by John DeWitt

All spiders produce silk in glands in their abdomens. Inside the spider, the silk is liquid, but it hardens when it meets the air. Any spider can produce several different kinds of silk for different purposes. Each silk gland produces only one kind of silk, which may be sticky, smooth, fluffy, or waterproof. There is silk for building webs, silk for draglines, silk for wrapping prey and silk for making egg cases. Each silk gland is connected by a long duct to an appendage called a spinneret, a sort of nozzle with many little holes at the end of the spider's abdomen.

Most spiders have six spinnerets, but some have only two, and some as many as eight. Spinnerets come in pairs, and each pair winds the many strands coming out of each nozzle into a thread with the necessary strength, thickness, and characteristics for the job it has to do. The spider can customize the strength and composition of silk strands. A strand may have one type of silk as the base, and another applied as a coating—for instance, for the sticky threads that capture insects in a web, sticky silk is applied over strong, web-building silk.

Spider silk is a remarkable substance. It is a protein, made of chains of amino acids. It is only one sixth as dense as steel and yet has greater tensile strength. It is exceptionally elastic and very light. One strand of spider silk long enough to encircle the earth would weigh only about 6 ounces. Though silk has many uses for the spider, it also requires a lot of energy to produce. The spider trades that energy for the energy conserved by capturing prey without chasing it. Many spiders eat their old webs before constructing new ones in order to recycle the silk.

About 80% of spiders spin webs for catching prey. Webs for catching prey come in many forms. Classic round webs are made by orb weavers whose building process is complex and prescribed. There are many other forms of webs. Tangled webs, such as the cobwebs we find in our homes, are disorganized and irregular. Funnel webs are flattened, open cones that narrow into tunnel-like holes where the spider lurks. Sheet webs, like the ones in the grass in the morning, are flat and horizontal, with the spider hiding somewhere at the edge. In general, the spiders that build similar types of webs are closely related in the same taxonomic family. All web-building spiders constantly monitor their webs by touching them. They can feel the impact when an insect is caught. Then the spider quickly runs out to bite and wrap the prey before it can struggle free. Spider webs have both sticky and smooth threads, and the spider avoids being caught in its own web by running only on the smooth lines.

Spiders that do not build webs still use silk in hunting. Wolf spiders pursue and capture their prey, laying down silken draglines to find their way home. Trap door spiders live in burrows surrounded by silken triplines. The burrow has a trap door made of soil and plant material glued together with silk. There is a silken hinge on one side, and the spider waits underneath for the tripline vibrations that tell it that prey is near. Then the trapdoor spider leaps out the door for the kill. Jumping spiders pounce on their prey, sometimes leaping fifty times the length of their own body, often from above. Before jumping, the spider attaches a silk line to the take off spot. If the spider misses, it can climb back for another try. Interestingly, the spiders that hunt and capture have much better eyesight than their web-building relatives.

Unlike many people, I am not afraid of most spiders. I let them live in my house, though when they get too numerous, I transport them outside. I like the look of a cobweb full of dead gnats and mosquitoes, and though I periodically vacuum up the webs, I let the spiders stay. If I walk a trail in the early morning, when other walkers have not gone before me, I frequently run into strands of spider silk strung over the path. I can feel the silk break as I pass, with a bit of regret at interfering with the spiders' remarkable work.

Caterpillars

Caterpillars seem to be everywhere at the end of August. Woolly bears are starting to appear. Fall webworms are busy eating leaves inside the silken tents they have spun around the ends of hardwood branches. Hickory tussock moths, their white furry bodies studded with tufts of long black bristles, crawl up the screens and over the lawn. Inchworms hang in the air on long threads, descending from the trees where they have been feeding to the ground where they will pupate. I am always astonished by caterpillars' diversity of size, form, and color.

A caterpillar is the larval form of the insect order Lepidoptera, moths and butterflies. In North America alone there are over 13,000 identified species. Of these about 12,000 are moths. We distinguish moths from butterflies by characteristics of the adult form. Moths generally fly at night, have feather-like antennae, rest with their wings spread, and pupate inside a cocoon woven of silk they manufacture in their bodies. Butterflies generally fly during the day, have thread-like antennae, rest with their wings folded, and pupate as chrysalises hung by an abdominal hook from a spun-silk button. In general, adult butterflies are more colorful than adult moths. But if you find a caterpillar, there is no way, other than raising it to adulthood, that you can tell by its physical appearance whether it will become a moth or a butterfly.

All insects have bodies that are divided into three parts—the head, the thorax, and the abdomen. The head includes the eyes, the antennae, and the mouthparts. The thorax is the middle region where the six legs and the wings are attached. The abdomen is the rearmost part, and contains the genitalia as well as other internal organs. A caterpillar, while its body parts are more difficult to distinguish by observation, has the same tripartite design including a head, a thorax and an abdomen.

If you look carefully at a caterpillar you can see that its body is made of segments rather like the segments of an earthworm or of an adult insect's abdomen. The first segment of every caterpillar is the head, which houses eyes, mouth, antennae, and the spinnerets. Spinnerets are spigot-like organs through which silk is discharged. The spinnerets are lost in the adult form of the insect. Behind the head are 13 body segments. The three thoracic segments carry the caterpillar's six true legs, each with a simple claw. These legs will become the six legs of the adult insect. The ten abdominal segments make up most of the length and weight of the caterpillar. On most caterpillars, the third through sixth segments bear eight paired prolegs, which are soft, hook-bearing organs that help the caterpillar grasp surfaces and walk. Inchworms, the caterpillars of a huge family called Geometrid moths, have only two pairs of prolegs set at the rear of their abdomens. Rather than walking flat on a surface, these caterpillars hump forward, drawing their hind end to meet their front.

A caterpillar is the growth phase of a moth or butterfly. Each moth or butterfly lays her eggs on a food plant appropriate for her species. Some species only eat one kind of plant. Monarch butterflies, for instance, lay their eggs only on milkweed. Other species may have a wide range of food plants. Tussock moths lay eggs on almost any woody or herbaceous plant. When the egg hatches, the tiny caterpillar that emerges begins to eat and grow. In the course of its growth, it passes through five or six molts, shedding its skin each time. The phase between molts is called an instar. The first instar hatches from the egg, and the last instar spins the cocoon or becomes the chrysalis where metamorphosis into the adult insect will take place. Some caterpillars increase their weight a thousandfold between the first and the last instars.

Caterpillars are an essential part of terrestrial food webs all over the world. They are an abundant, protein-rich food that many songbirds feed to their young throughout the nesting season. Just about every vertebrate and non-vertebrate animal group has a number of species that prey on caterpillars and control their numbers. Many simply eat the caterpillars. Others, including many wasps, parasitize caterpillars by laying eggs in their bodies, thus providing food sources for their own developing young. Without predaceous birds, beetles, wasps, spiders, and many other animals, caterpillars would consume much of our crops and defoliate our forests.

Because they have so many predators, caterpillars have evolved various defensive strategies. Some are cleverly camouflaged to look like a part of the plant on which they feed. These caterpillars may look like twigs, buds, bits of bark, small fruits, or tendrils. Another visual defense is to sport large eyespots or false heads that fool predators into thinking the caterpillar is a snake or other sizeable animal.

Many caterpillars employ chemical defenses. Some are covered with soft hairs that contain irritating chemicals. Others are brightly colored to warn predators that they are distasteful. Some concentrate toxins from their food plants, making themselves unpalatable or toxic. Some have venom-tipped spines. There are tropical caterpillars so poisonous that they have caused human deaths. In general, brightly colored caterpillars are advertising their unappetizing taste or toxic qualities to predators.

Some caterpillars use their spinnerets to weave silken shelters or nests. Tent caterpillars and fall webworms spin large communal roosts and feeding zones. Leaf roller caterpillars attach silk to both sides of a leaf, and then pull it tight to create a safe refuge. Many caterpillars continually spin a thread of silk as they move, creating both an anchor and a lifeline. When disturbed they can spring into space and rappel away from the danger. Once the threat is past, they can climb the thread once again, consuming it as they go, and return to feeding.

Despite the fact that caterpillars are voracious eaters and sometimes damage my plants, I like seeing them in my yard and garden. There are some, like cutworms and tomato hornworms, which are so destructive that I kill them on sight. But I enjoy most caterpillars for their beauty, their variety, and the purposeful way they pursue their lives. It is interesting to reflect that the lives of these animals are so different from the lives of mammals like me that I can't begin to guess from their juvenile appearance what they will look like when they become adults.

Lichens

Everywhere you look on Isle au Haut you find lichens. They stipple granite boulders and ledges, make bristly crusts on soil, cling to the bark of trees, festoon the dead branches of spruce trees, and sprout from rotting logs. Lichens grow on the hood of my partner's old Ford Bronco. They cover the roof of a friend's house with bright orange splotches. They come in various sizes, forms, textures, and colors. What are lichens?

Old Man's Beard - Photo by John DeWitt

Lichens are dual organisms. Each lichen incorporates both a fungus and a photosynthetic organism. This photosynthesizer can be either an alga, which is a one-celled plant, or a blue-green alga, which is a kind of bacterium. The fungus and the alga have a symbiotic relationship: each does something for the other. The fungus provides structure and shelter for the alga, and the alga provides food for the fungus. Each species of lichen comprises a particular species of fungus and a particular species of alga, and each species has unique, recognizable characteristics. If you separate the fungus from the alga in the lab, each can grow separately, and each looks different from the lichen in which it originated.

Lichens come in several different forms. Crustose lichens, the flat, spreading, irregular circles you see on rocks, are firmly attached to a solid surface and cannot be easily scraped off. Foliose lichens are also flat, but are attached only at certain spots and grow spreading, layered scales or flakes that can break off. Fruticose lichens grow upright like tiny, many-branched bushes, or form long filaments that drape from branches. Reindeer moss, the pale green tangle we often see on the ground along trails, and old man's beard, the grey-green tufts that adorn our spruce trees, are examples of fruticose lichens. There are more than 3,500 species of lichens in North America.

Lungwort - Photo by Marnie Davis

Lichens are nature's pioneers. They can take hold on inhospitable rock surfaces, infiltrating cracks and filling small depressions. As they die, they leave detritus that adds to the minerals from the rock and traps dust and silt, creating pockets of new soil where mosses and tiny vascular plants can sprout. Lichens spearhead life on disturbed or sandy soils. They establish themselves on tundra and in deserts, providing structure and adding organic matter. In our northern spruce forests they play an important role in retaining soil moisture, trapping seeds, and adding nutrients to the soils.

Lichens have a number of extraordinary adaptations. They dry out quickly, becoming brittle and lifeless. When this happens, all metabolic activity and all molecular reactions cease, as if the lichens were dead. They can stay in this state for months.

Then as soon as it rains, the lichens become spongy and flexible and immediately start to live again. Lichens are able to survive in both the coldest and the hottest places on earth. They are the dominant vegetation in the Arctic and Antarctic, as well as in the hottest deserts. Humans have sent lichens into outer space, where they were exposed to cosmic radiation, huge fluctuations in temperature, and the vacuum of space. Once back on earth the lichens grew again, healthy and undamaged.

Sunburst Lichen - Photo By John DeWitt

Despite their amazing resilience in extreme conditions, lichens are exceptionally sensitive to pollution. They are often used by scientists to monitor air quality. It is no coincidence that only a few lichens grow in urban places where air quality is poor. A vibrant assortment of lichens such as we have on Isle au Haut is a sign of environmental health. Lichens are easily harmed by hikers, rock climbers, and off-road vehicles. They grow very slowly. If you crunch through a patch of dry lichens, you may have set their growth back 100 years.

Sexual reproduction is a major challenge for a species that contains two different species. The fungi in lichens reproduce by growing fruiting bodies that look like little open cups or flasks. If you look carefully at the lichens spreading over rocks, you can see these fruiting bodies. When ripe, they explode millions of spores into the air. The algae in lichens do not reproduce in concert with the fungi, so in order for a new lichen to be formed, a spore from the fungus must land in a place where it happens to encounter cells of its algal partner, a slim chance at best. It is not surprising that most lichens can also reproduce vegetatively. This means that they reproduce by budding or fragmentation. Many lichens shed little balls of fungal cells that enclose a few algal cells. These balls can grow into new lichens. Or a broken fragment of lichen can get pulverized and reconstitute itself into a new lichen.

Part of the beauty of lichens comes from their wide variety of colors—yellow, green, orange, red, white, black, brown, gray. But why should lichens be brightly colored? Flowers are colored to attract pollinators, birds to attract mates, butterflies to announce to predators that they are distasteful or poisonous. The most colorful lichens grow in sunny places, so the reason for their colors must be connected to sunlight. The blue-green algae that are part of many lichens are easily damaged by ultraviolet light. Scientists believe that the fungal components of lichens growing in exposed places have evolved colors to protect their algal partners from damage.

Next time you go out hiking, take time to stop and admire the variety of lichens you will see. If you crouch down you will observe the intricate branching of the reindeer moss, the bright colors of the British soldiers, the overlapping shapes and patterns of the crustose and foliose lichens on the rocks. Lichens are among the least understood, most overlooked, and most diverse organisms on earth. Their lives may go on beneath our feet, but they don't have to go on beneath our notice.

Double-crested Cormorants
(Phalacrocorax auritus)

Last week I saw my first V-shaped flock of cormorants heading south to their wintering grounds in the southern United States. Many people look up and think those straggling vees are Canada geese. Some of them are—but along the coast, most are cormorants.

Cormorants, like geese, cranes, pelicans, and swans, use the V-formation during migration to boost the energy efficiency of their flight. Each bird takes advantage of the upwash of air from the wings of the bird ahead of it, thus reducing drag and increasing lift. The bird at the tip of a V is working harder than all the others, but it is not the dominant bird or the permanent leader. It rotates back when tired, letting another bird take its place. The V-shaped flock achieves an increase in distance traveled of 70% over an individual bird, because individuals tire sooner and need to come down to rest. The V-formation also helps birds flying together to see each other and communicate easily.

Double-crested cormorants are native to the entire United States, much of Canada, and parts of Mexico. They are long-necked, blackish aquatic birds with long, hooked beaks, bare orange skin around their faces and chins, and a four foot wingspan. They inhabit both fresh and salt water inland and along the coast. They are gregarious, flocking with other cormorants and often resting with gulls and sea ducks on ledges and rocky outcroppings. Their diet consists almost entirely of fish, which they catch by diving. They swim powerfully when hunting, using their webbed feet for propulsion, and diving as deep as 100 feet. They grab fish with their beaks. When a cormorant catches a small fish, it eats the fish under water. But when it catches a larger fish, the cormorant carries it to the surface, flipping it up and catching it until the fish is pointed headfirst down the cormorant's throat for swallowing.

Cormorant feathers lack the buoyant oil that waterproofs most sea birds' feathers. That is why cormorants float so low in the water. Often we see only a sinuous neck while the body is hidden below the waterline. The lack of buoyant oil on cormorants' feathers helps them to dive deep, often hunting along the bottom in search of prey. After fishing, a cormorant's feathers are wet and heavy, which is why we often see cormorants standing on rocks with their wings spread out to dry like laundry.

Cormorants reach breeding age at three years. They nest in crowded colonies, often with other species of seabirds. Our coastal cormorants nest on remote shoreland or offshore islands. During the nesting season cormorants have two curly crests, bright blue eyes, and vivid orange throats. All these features are lost after the breeding season. The male chooses the nest site and advertises for a mate with wing-waving displays that show off the bright orange skin around his head. Once a pair bond has been formed, the two cormorants either make or refurbish a big nest of sticks, grass, and all kinds of debris. The male brings nesting materials to the female, who constructs the nest.

The parents share the job of incubating three to seven blue eggs for almost four weeks. The young hatch out naked and blind. Before the babies have feathers their parents must shade them from the hot sun with their wings and bring them water, which they pour into the babies' mouths from their beaks. Young cormorants grow quickly on a rich diet of regurgitated fish brought to them by both parents. Once they are able to leave the nest, all the young birds in a colony join forces in a big group called a crèche. They roam about together as a social group and return to their own nests only to be fed. A cormorant nesting colony is a cacophony of sounds—the young begging and squawking, the adults grunting somewhat like pigs. Young cormorants learn to fly at about five weeks, and are completely independent of their parents at around ten weeks old.

Historically, cormorants have been blamed for preying on fish species valued by fishermen and aquaculturists. Humans have hunted them relentlessly for centuries. By the turn of the nineteenth century cormorants were eradicated from New England. They were beginning to make a comeback in the twentieth century, but suffered from thin eggshells resulting from DDT residues in the fish they ate. Since 1972, when DDT was banned, cormorants have made a strong recovery. Today they are a big problem for catfish farmers in Mississippi. But all summer I enjoy watching cormorants diving gracefully, tossing fish in the air and swallowing them, and drying their wings on the rocks. And I am always touched by the bittersweet message they deliver in autumn as they head south in long, wavering vees against the sky.

Fall

Dragonflies
(Anax junius)

Ohne day this past week I stood at the edge of a long field of grass and milkweed to watch a feeding swarm of dragonflies. It was late afternoon, and I was on the eastern side of the field looking west into the low sun. There were hundreds of large dragonflies, their bodies backlit and shimmering as they patrolled the field. I noticed that there were a myriad of tiny flecks of light filling the air, and realized that the dragonflies were feeding on a hatch of small insects. It was a beautiful sight.

Photo by Joan Handel

In the next few days, I visited the field several times with binoculars, and identified the dragonflies as common green darners, Anax junius. I found two of them, a male and a female, hanging companionably next to each other in a bayberry bush at the field's edge, and I studied them closely. The green darner is about three inches long with clear wings and a bright green head and thorax. The male's abdomen is a deep purplish blue, and the female's a dull red.

Dragonflies, together with their relatives the damselflies, include about 7,000 species. This sounds like a large number, but compared to beetles, with over 400,000 species, dragonflies present a manageable field of study. Like most insects, they have a fascinating life story. We are familiar with the adults, which grace our ponds, meadows, streams, and wetlands during the summer and fall. This adult phase, lasting from a couple of weeks to several months, is only a brief final chapter in the dragonfly's life.

A green darner spends up to three years as a crablike nymph called a naiad in shallow water, where it hunts and grows. A dragonfly nymph eats thousands of mosquito larvae and other small organisms, capturing them with jointed, projectile jaws. It sheds its skin many times, just like a shedding lobster. Dragonflies and lobsters are both members of the phylum Arthropoda, which includes insects, crustaceans, and spiders. All of these animals have hard skins called exoskeletons, and must shed in order to grow.

When a nymph is ready to make its final molt and become an adult dragonfly it crawls upward out of the water onto a twig or stone, locks its legs onto its perch, and splits the skin of its thorax. It arches out of its skin, and inflates its new body, pumping blood first into its wings and then into the slender tube of its abdomen. At this point the adult dragonfly is soft and vulnerable, at the mercy of fortune until it hardens and flies away, transformation complete. You can often find the shed skins of dragonfly nymphs near the edges of ponds and streams.

Reborn as an elegant, winged predator, the dragonfly spends a lot of time hunting, capturing other insects on the wing. Dragonflies are amazingly efficient predators, catching more than 95 percent of their targeted prey. They have a full field of vision and can see their entire surroundings at all times because their large, compound eyes wrap almost completely around their heads. Each eye has thirty thousand facets, each facet looking at the surroundings at a slightly different angle. Dragonflies can fly up to thirty miles per hour, hover, dive, fly upside down and backwards, and keep focus on one prey insect in a large swarm. They can control each of their four wings individually, making it possible for them to pivot instantaneously in midair, maneuvering unerringly as they pursue prey. They attack from behind and below, which gives them the advantage of surprise. A dragonfly can eat hundreds of mosquitos, gnats, or small flies in a single day. Thank you, dragonfly.

But the main job of adult dragonflies is to mate and lay eggs. A male green darner simply grabs a passing female out of the air and locks the end of his abdomen into a keyhole-like receptacle on the back of her head. The female locks her abdomen into the male's genitals on his underside, making their two bodies into a closed circle. He transfers a packet of sperm into her body. When you see two dragonflies in flight in this "wheel" position, that's what they are doing. The male stays in the wheel position with the female as she lays her eggs. She lays eggs individually, either in plant stems just under the water, or by tapping eggs onto the surface of the water one by one with the tip of her abdomen. The eggs remain hidden in the plant stems or sink to the bottom. The eggs hatch into nymphs, beginning another generation of dragonflies in the diverse community of organisms on the bottom of the pond. These nymphs will, like their parents, live three years in the water before hatching into adult dragonflies.

Scientists have recently determined that several species of dragonfly, including the green darner, are migratory in their northern range. Among northern green darners there are both resident and migratory populations. The resident green darners live their entire life cycle from egg through adult insect in the north. The migratory dragonfly population alternates generations from north to south. One generation, born in the north, moves south in swarms during the fall to mate, lay eggs, and die in warmer places. Their young will emerge in the south and move north in the spring to mate, lay eggs, and die. The emerging young from this generation will move south in the fall to complete their life cycle. Fall swarms like the one I saw last week are on the move, refueling as they fly south to avoid the oncoming cold. The green darner may journey southward as much as four hundred miles and extend its life by several months before breeding in its southern habitat.

It is a singular experience to encounter a swarm of any kind of migratory creature in the midst of its journey. Among those I have observed are tree swallows, monarch butterflies, horseshoe crabs, American eels, ladybugs, and green darner dragonflies. When I see a migratory swarm, I know that I am getting a view into a world I can never inhabit. The instinctual forces that drive individual animals to migrate are not present in my human character. I can only stand still to witness and marvel at the beauty and adaptive value of migration.

$\mathcal{F}$ield $\mathcal{C}$rickets
(*Gryllus* spp.)

September is the month of the cricket. These large, dark insects that have been crawling quietly about in our yards and fields all summer eating seeds, plants, and other insects, suddenly begin to sing as summer comes to an end. Crickets' days are numbered as winter approaches. When I walk my dog in the fields this month, the peaceful silence of summer afternoons is replaced by the peaceful sound of chirping male crickets.

Autumn is the mating season for crickets. Males establish territories, and attract females by rubbing their forewings together to create the familiar 3-pulse chirp we hear. One forewing has a sharp ridge called a scraper, and the other a series of ridged veins called a file. Rubbing the two together is like rubbing a fingernail over the teeth of a comb—it makes a sound. As the males chirp, the females wander about listening to their songs. Eventually each female chooses the male whose chirp she finds most appealing. She approaches him and touches him with her antennae, which inspires him to give another, softer courting chirp, and then the couple proceeds to mate.

Sometimes, an aggressive male cricket intrudes on another's territory, and a fight may ensue. Fighting male crickets give a loud chirp different from the mating call and the courtship song. They fight fiercely, and may lose legs or even kill each other. (In southern China, cricket fighting is a sport, with champion crickets and high stakes gambling.) At other times a non-territorial wandering male cricket may lurk silently at the edges of a singer's territory, trying to intercept a female and mate with her before the resident male can woo her. These crickets are called satellite males. Interestingly, this satellite behavior is genetic—males who use this mating strategy pass it on to their offspring, so there are always both calling males and satellite males in the cricket population.

A male cricket transfers his sperm to the female in a little packet called a spermatophore. The cricket couple moves into position with the help of their antennae and little hairlike structures on the ends of their abdomens. The female mounts the male, and he bends his abdomen upward to attach his spermatophore to a receptacle on the underside of her abdomen. After all the effort of finding a mate and wooing her, the male may at this point lose his chance to father the next generation. If his lady love is hungry, she may just eat his spermatophore and wander off to find another mate.

A female cricket is equipped with a ¾ inch long syringe-like tube called an ovipositor at the end of her abdomen. This feature makes it easy to tell male and female crickets apart. Once the female has used a spermatophore to fertilize her eggs, she inserts her ovipositor into the soil and injects her one hundred or more eggs, one at a time, into the earth where they overwinter.

The next spring, the cricket eggs hatch into nymphs, which are smaller and simpler versions of adult crickets. They molt, or shed their skins, eight or more times during the summer, each time becoming larger and more like an adult cricket. At their last molt, near the end of summer, they become mature adults with wings and fully developed reproductive systems. This style of insect development is called incomplete metamorphosis, and is used by crickets and their relatives—grasshoppers, katydids, and locusts—as well as a number of other insect groups.

All insects are cold-blooded and must have some way of surviving winter. For crickets, overwintering eggs assure the next generation. All the adults die off when the hard frost comes. For me, the song of the field cricket is tinged with sadness because it is a swan song—the last act in the small drama of the cricket's inconspicuous life.

Lobsters
(Homarus americanus)

Part 1: Lobster Anatomy

My partner Albert has a small string of thirty lobster traps, and I'm his sternman. All summer and fall we go out to haul twice a week. We often take friends, relatives, and their children along with us. I spend some of my time on the boat teaching our passengers about lobsters and all the other sea life that comes up in the traps. I find it amazing, as I look out over the expanse of water studded with hundreds of buoys, most of which are marking pairs of traps, how many lobsters must be crawling around on the bottom. Most of those traps are hauled every few days, and the lobsters just keep on coming.

The Maine lobster, Homarus americanus, is in the phylum Arthropoda, which means "jointed leg." The arthropods include insects, spiders and their relatives, and crustaceans. There are many different kinds of crustaceans. Barnacles are crustaceans. Lots of tiny creatures like the jumpy amphipods that live in the seaweed wrack line and the innumerable pink "sea fleas" that eat our bait and sometimes cover the washboard on the lobster boat are crustaceans. But the best-known crustaceans are the decapods, which is from Latin meaning "ten legs." Shrimp, crayfish, crabs and lobsters all belong to this order. In the case of the lobster, the ten legs consist of four pairs of walking legs and a pair of claws.

All crustaceans have a shell called an exoskeleton that covers a body divided into three regions called, as in insects, the head, the thorax and the abdomen. In the lobster the head and thorax are fused under the hard upper shell, or carapace, and are known as the cephalothorax. In order to grow, the lobster must shed its shell regularly. Before shedding, the lobster grows a new, leathery shell under the old one. If the lobster has lost any appendages new ones begin to regenerate with the new shell. Before shedding, the lobster withdraws the blood from its muscles, causing its body to shrivel inside the old shell. Then the lobster inflates itself with water, forcing the old shell to open between the carapace and the tail. The lobster in its new, soft shell pulls its entire body—antennae, legs, tail and all—through the opening, leaving the old shell behind. At this point the lobster is very vulnerable to attack, and must hide while its new shell hardens.

The next time you sit down to a lobster dinner, take a minute to look at its anatomy from head to tail—or rather from cephalothorax to telson. The lobster's head includes two eyes, two pairs of antennae, a complicated set of mouthparts, and the spiny rostrum, which sticks out from the foremost tip of the carapace and protects the eyes. The eyes are stalked and compound, and the lobster can move them about. They are adapted to low-light environments, but scientists are not sure how well lobsters can actually see.

The lobster's most important sense organs are the antennae and the mouthparts. The long antennae are tactile organs with which the lobster feels its way in its underwater world. The short antennae, or antennules, are the "nose" of the lobster. They are bifurcated and covered with tiny hairs that are extremely sensitive to chemicals, especially proteins, in the water. Lobsters flick these antennules frequently, sniffing the water. You can observe this in the lobster tank at the supermarket. The lobster's mouthparts and legs are also covered with hairs. These hairs are for tasting. The lobster probes with its legs in the sediment, and brings food items to its mouth. The mouth makes the final decision whether or not to swallow.

At the base of the antennae you can see two small, nozzle-like bumps through which the lobster excretes urine. Kids of all ages on our boat are astonished to learn that lobsters pee out of their faces. Lobster pee is not just a waste product. It also contains pheromones, which are chemicals used to communicate with other lobsters. This adaptation makes it possible for a lobster to broadcast messages forward into the water when it meets another lobster. The lobster can send a number of messages in its pee—"I'm a male," or "I'm a female," or "If you come any closer, I'll attack you," or "I'm looking for a mate."

Now take a look at your lobster's claws and its walking legs. The two claws are different from each other. The larger crusher claw has bumpy teeth, which the lobster uses to crush hard foods such as snails and clams. The smaller tearing claw has jagged teeth for ripping up food. These claws are incredibly strong. If a lobster manages to "bite" when you are handling it, you might have to wait for it to let go because it's almost impossible to pry the claw open. Albert lost a thumbnail last summer to a lobster bite. Behind the claws are the legs. The first two pairs have little claws on the ends, which a lobster uses both for walking and for feeding. The rearmost two pairs of legs are pointy on the ends, and are for walking only.

Now we come to the tail, which is a misnomer. It is actually the abdomen. The abdominal segments are jointed and they are controlled by strong muscles. For most people, the powerful abdominal muscles are the choicest morsels of the lobster's meat. When a living lobster encounters danger, it uses these muscles to flip its tail rapidly, which sends it shooting backward through the water.

On the underside of the abdomen are five pairs of fin-like swimmerets. The first pair will tell you whether the lobster is a male or a female. If it is a male, the first pair of swimmerets is hard, with a groove down the inner side of each one. When pressed together, the grooves form a tube through which the male can pass a spermatophore into the female's body when he mates with her. If the lobster is a female, the first pair of swimmerets is small, soft, and feathery. The rest of the swimmerets are used for circulating water around the lobster's body, and in the case of the female, for holding and ventilating her eggs during the months that she carries them on her underside. The swimmerets of the female lobster are quite hairy, and these hairs help the female to keep her eggs attached. Finally, there are the five tail flippers—the central telson and the outer uropods, which form the fan of the lobster's tail and provide a powerful paddle blade when the lobster is flipping its tail to propel itself backwards during its escape response.

There is a lot more to learn, but your lobster is getting cold. Enough lobster anatomy. Dig in.

Part 2: Lobster Ecology and Life Cycle

Lobsters are certainly plentiful in the waters around Isle au Haut. In the past ten years, lobster landings have risen exponentially. The bottom of the ocean must be swarming with these creatures that crawl all summer into our traps and form the basis of our coastal economy. While fishermen are going about the business of catching them and selling them, the lobsters are going about their complex lives.

The Maine lobster, Homarus americanus, is an omnivorous hunter and scavenger that lives in the waters of the western Atlantic from North Carolina to Labrador.

Lobsters are most abundant and largest in colder waters. Lobsters can be found from the intertidal zone to as deep as 1,500 feet, but are mostly found in depths from 10 to 160 feet. In the summer, lobsters prefer onshore habitats where the water is warmer. As the ocean surface cools in the fall, they move to deeper waters where temperatures are more stable. Lobsters grow by shedding their shells, a process which becomes less frequent as the lobster gets older.

A lobster becomes legal to catch in Maine when its carapace length (as opposed to its total body length) reaches 3 ¼ inches. At this time it is five to seven years old and sheds once a year. Sexual maturity for a lobster comes at about the same time that it reaches legal size. Most of these lobsters molt in early to mid summer and become the "shedders" caught in such huge numbers by Maine lobstermen. Most shedders never get a chance to reproduce. But a few females will not be caught until they are carrying eggs. Once a female becomes an "egger," a fisherman must notch one of her tail flippers and release her back to the wild. Her notch will last through several sheds, and she will be illegal to keep as long as the notch is visible. A lobsterman can lose his license for selling a notched female to a dealer. Most likely a notched female will live to breed again. This brings us to the fascinating sex life of the lobster.

Sexually mature male lobsters are aggressive and territorial. They compete with each other for the best hidey-holes from which to attract and woo receptive females. Females compete for access to desirable males, so the largest and most aggressive females have first choice of mates. In order to mate, a female must first molt her shell. Molting is stimulated by the warming of the seawater, so lobsters usually mate in early summer. When she is ready to molt, a mature female selects the most aggressive and often the largest male with the safest lair. The female releases a pheromone into the water, which calms the male's aggression and induces him to perform a stately court-ship dance, waving his closed claws. Then he leads her into his lair and waits for her to shed her hard shell.

When she emerges in her new, soft shell, he mates with her, belly to belly, passing a packet of sperm called a spermatophore into a seminal receptacle in her body. He protects her inside his lair until her new shell is hard enough to keep her safe from other lobsters and to keep other males from mating with her. If he is a desirable mate, other females will be waiting outside his door, and he will usher in the next female waiting in line for his attentions.

A mated female carries the spermatophore inside her body until she is ready to fertilize her eggs. She can store the sperm for more than a year if she chooses. When the female is ready to lay her eggs, she flips on her back, and cups her tail. The eggs pass through the seminal receptacle, where they are fertilized. She extrudes them onto the underside of her tail along with an adhesive that glues them to her swimmerets. Usually, she extrudes eggs in the late summer. She carries the eggs for almost a year, constantly fanning them with her swimmerets to keep them oxygenated. The tiny larval lobsters molt more than thirty times inside their eggs before hatching. As the eggs hatch the female releases the larvae, waving her tail to set them free. They are attracted by light and float up to the surface, joining the plankton. Of the 10,000 eggs released by the average female lobster, only about ten will survive the planktonic phase.

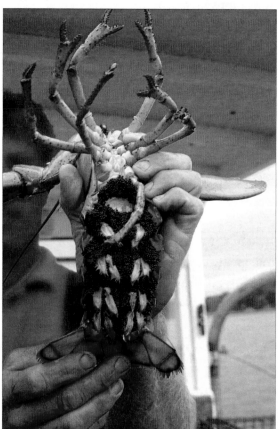

A female lobster carrying eggs. Photo By Joan Handel

A newly hatched larval lobster looks more like a mosquito than like an adult lobster. It feeds on other tiny organisms in the plankton and, if it is not itself eaten by another tiny predator, it will molt three more times while floating in the plankton near the water's surface. Each time it molts, it gains more of the features of an adult lobster. At the fourth molt, it transforms to a half inch juvenile called a "superman lobster" because it swims with its claws outstretched ahead of its body. At this point it loses its preference for light and swims to the bottom looking for a place to settle. Baby lobsters prefer cobble bottoms where they can hide among the stones, and may rise back into the plankton and resettle several times before finding the right habitat.

Lobsters are omnivores. They hunt as well as scavenge for their food. When they are tiny they avoid predation by staying hidden under cobble or in seaweed. At this stage, which lasts about a year, they filter the water for microscopic food particles. In the year that passes between the first molt inside the egg to the time when it ventures out of hiding, a lobster has shed more than forty times. Until it reaches about four inches long, the lobster stays in areas where it can quickly hide. At about four inches a lobster is strong and agile enough to crack small mollusks and urchins and to fend off predators. The lobster becomes increasingly mobile and can roam the bottom more safely. Despite the fact that small lobsters are not yet sexually mature, their behavior is very similar to that of adults, although they shed more frequently, usually twice a year.

Lobsters live a long time. No one is exactly sure how long, because the lobster has no anatomical feature which, like the growth rings in a tree trunk, reveals its age to humans. But scientists estimate that lobsters can live more than sixty years. The largest lobster on record weighed 44.4 pounds. It was about four feet long.

Usually when people think about lobster, they imagine a dinner plate holding a red, spiny, cooked creature—formidable to crack but full of delicious meat. I like to think of lobsters floating in the plankton, hiding in the cobble, roaming the bottom, and especially courting each other under the sea. My favorite part of lobstering is catching an egg-bearing female, notching her, and releasing her into the water knowing that she will probably live a long, safe, and productive life.

Bucks and Their Antlers
(Odocoileus virginianus)

I was driving a dirt road the other day and stopped to watch three white-tailed bucks feeding in the huckleberry bushes at the roadside. Our island deer are quite tame. They often stand gazing at me for some minutes before flipping their tails and bounding off into the forest. I had time to observe this trio and note their antlers. One was an eight-point buck, one a four-point buck, and one had only little spikes for antlers. It made me wonder about bucks and their antlers, and why antlers vary so much from one buck to another.

Photo by John DeWitt

Deer antlers are made of bone. They are the fastest growing bone tissue known to science, adding as much as a half-inch in length a day. Once antlers have finished growing, the bone tissue dies and becomes so hard that people throughout history have used it to make tools such as needles and awls, and weapons such as spears and arrowheads.

Antlers differ from horns in several ways. Antlers are shed and regrown every year, while horns grow throughout the lives of the bearers. Antlers are primarily grown by male members of the deer family, including deer, elk, and moose, while horns are grown by both sexes of the cattle family, including cows, goats, bison, and sheep. Antlers grow and die each year, while horns are made of living bone sheathed in layers of keratin, a protein that is the basis of hooves, hair, feathers, claws, and fingernails. Antlers probably evolved to facilitate communication and dominance during the mating season, while horns probably evolved to protect the skull.

The yearly cycle of antler development is controlled by the length of daylight. In the spring the days lengthen and trigger hormones that stimulate antler growth. The growing antlers are covered in a soft skin called velvet that supplies oxygen, nutrients, and blood to the fast-growing bone. During this time of rapid growth, antlers are very sensitive to touch and vulnerable to injury. In late summer, shorter days trigger the production of testosterone, which stops antler growth. The velvet dies, then the bone hardens and dies. The velvet begins to slough off and the bucks speed the process by rubbing it off on saplings, creating polished antlers ready for the mating season. When rubbing off the velvet, bucks are also marking the "rubs" with the scent of the velvet and the scent from glands in their foreheads. Bucks return to the same rubs again and again, concentrating their scent and maintaining it on their antlers, which broadcast the scent in the wind.

As fall progresses towards winter, bucks are flooded with testosterone. It causes their necks to grow extra muscle and swell in preparation for the battles of the mating season. Testosterone also makes bucks aggressive and eager to prove their desirability to does. Bucks spar with each other for territory and dominance, clashing their antlers together until one buck overpowers the other. Bucks also display their antlers, attempting to impress does with their vigor and health. Does choose mates based on whose scent dominates the air, and whose strength and size wins the contests. Usually only the dominant bucks will be chosen. These bucks will father most of the fawns in any given season.

The length, size, and branching of a buck's antlers depend on age, nutrition, and genetics. Bucks reach full maturity at five or six years. A yearling buck often grows small spike antlers. Each year thereafter the antlers get bigger and more elaborate until full maturity. Nutrition also plays an important role. Antlers grow from nubbins called pedicles attached to the skull. If a buck fawn receives good nutrition the pedicles will be large, and the buck will grow larger antlers throughout life. Every year the potential size of the rack can be realized only if the buck is well-nourished. In times of deprivation body growth takes precedence over antler growth.

After the mating season is over in December or January bucks shed their antlers. One would think that with the number of deer in the woods, it would be easy to find antlers on the forest floor. But dropped antlers are an important source of calcium and phosphorus for mice, squirrels, rabbits, and voles whose rugged incisors are strong enough to scrape away the hard antler bone. A fallen antler is quickly consumed. If you ever do find an antler, look carefully for the marks of tiny teeth, which will tell you that someone has been there before you.

Antlers are heavy, unwieldy, and cost a lot of energy to produce. Bucks do very well without antlers for part of the year, and does never need them at all. In order to be worth having, antlers must provide a great advantage for bucks in mating success and the maintenance of a social structure.

Deer are social animals. In the depths of winter they congregate into herds that include bucks, does, and young deer. For the rest of the year, mature bucks live separately from does and young deer. In the late spring, after the new fawns are born, related does with their fawns and yearlings form groups. Small groups of bucks share the does' range but feed and bed down independently. Within their small groups, bucks establish dominance hierarchies and get along with each other without much friction. The three bucks I saw together were a part of a group and were comfortable together. But as the mating season approaches they will begin sparring more and more frequently and become more territorial and aggressive. Perhaps the eight-pointer will dominate the four-pointer and the spikehorn and will win the favor of the does in the area. But there may be another buck nearby whose health and virility and antlers prove more irresistible. Bucks carry the burden of their antlers and engage in combat, but in the end it is the does that decide whose genes are carried into the future.

Common Loons
(Gavia immer)

All summer as I work outdoors in my garden overlooking the sea, I hear the haunting tremolo calls of loons. I always stop to listen to this sound, which seems as if it comes from another world, ancient and mysterious. Indeed, loons are one of the oldest orders of birds, having remained virtually unchanged for more than 35 million years, while the earth and its climate have changed around them.

Common loons are big, heavy birds weighing up to thirteen pounds, with four-foot wingspans. They are long-lived—up to thirty years—and do not reach sexual maturity until they are three years old. Most do not actually breed successfully until they are at least six years old. In breeding plumage, loons are intricately patterned black and white with bright red eyes and a strong, black bill. In their winter plumage, they are white beneath and grey-brown above.

Loons live in both fresh and salt water. During their breeding season, they range throughout most of Canada and the northern United States, preferring large, clear, pristine lakes. When the lakes freeze they migrate to their wintering grounds along the Atlantic, Pacific, and Gulf coasts and in southern lakes and rivers.

Another name for the common loon is the great northern diver. Unlike most birds, which have hollow bones that reduce their weight in flight, loons have solid bones. This helps them to dive deep. Their powerful feet are set far back on their bodies so they can swim swiftly under water, pursuing their prey with extraordinary agility. A diving loon expels the air from its lungs, flattens its feathers, and presses its wings close to its body. When a loon catches a fish, it often brings it to the surface and repeatedly tosses and catches it to orient it favorably for swallowing it head first. An adult loon needs to eat two pounds of fish every day.

On land, because of their weight and the location of their feet, loons are ungainly creatures. They can barely walk. Except for mating and nesting they spend their entire lives in the water. They need water runways at least ¼ mile long to get up enough speed to lift their heavy bodies off the water's surface and take flight. Though loons have a hard time taking off, once airborne they can fly 70 miles per hour.

Because they prefer clean, undisturbed lakes, loons have been driven out of many of their traditional nesting lakes by development, pollution, and acid rain. After severe declines in loon populations in the late 20th century, people initiated many local restoration efforts that have helped loon populations to rebound. Maine, with its huge, undeveloped, lake-studded north woods is second only to Minnesota in U.S. nesting loon population, with about 4,300 pairs.

Male loons leave the coast in late April and arrive at inland lakes just after ice-out to establish territories. Experienced males often return to previous nesting areas, while young males look for territories close to the lakes where they were raised. The females arrive shortly after the males. Loons are serially monogamous, with most pair bonds lasting about five years. Research shows that they are actually more loyal to their preferred lakes than to their mates. Pairs do not winter together, but reunite at lakes in the spring.

Young loons and adults who do not find mates spend their summer on the coast where they will not be in conflict with fiercely territorial breeding loons. That is why we coastal Mainers see both adult loons in breeding plumage and juveniles in their grey-brown and white plumage off our shores in the summertime.

After performing elaborate courtship rituals, a loon pair chooses a nest site on an island or secluded cove in a lake. The loons build a nest of grass right next to the water so they can easily slip in without having to walk on land. The pair mates on the nest and shares the four-week incubation of two eggs. The downy black chicks take to the water within hours of hatching in early June. A day or two later, the parents shepherd them to a safe "nursery" area where the fishing is good.

In their first weeks of life, baby loons are completely dependent on their parents for food and protection. They cannot regulate their body temperature or dive competently. They often ride on their parents' backs or under their wings. Riding instead of swimming allows the chicks to stay warm, be safe from underwater predators like snapping turtles and northern pike, and avoid the exertion of keeping up with their parents. By about four weeks old, the chicks have molted into their first adult feathers. They can maintain their temperature, and they learn to dive and fish. As the young become more self-sufficient, the parents spend less time with them.

By mid-August, adult loons gather into groups preparing to migrate south or to the coast, and juvenile loons are increasingly independent. Adults undergo a partial molt into their brown and white winter plumage and migrate in September. Some migrate only a short distance to the coast, while others fly long distances southward. The juveniles migrate in late fall, just before ice makes the lakes uninhabitable. By early winter we coastal Mainers are seeing loons in all stages of their lives—juveniles, non-breeding adults, and mature adults.

Common loons are the iconic birds of northern forest lakes. Their dramatic plumage and affinity for the most untouched wild places call to people's yearnings for a wilder, simpler world. The thrilling sound of the loon's tremolos, yodels, and wails awakens our sense of wonder. Though we think of the loon as a bird of lakes, we on the coast are privileged to enjoy loons all year long in all plumages.

Wild Turkeys
(Meleagris gallopavo)

When I moved to Isle au Haut in the late 1990s, there were lots of wild turkeys on the island. Local lore tells us that an islander introduced them in the 1970s. In the absence of significant predators turkeys multiplied beyond anyone's wildest dream. In wintertime, trails and fields were crisscrossed with turkey tracks in the snow. Turkeys frequented people's porches and feeders looking for food. Sometimes in the spring turkeys blocked traffic. The open space of the road provided a good arena for a tom to display for a rapt audience of hens ready to choose a mate. They were wild turkeys, but not very.

Photo By Joan Handel

Then, in the early 2000s, eastern coyotes migrated to Isle au Haut and established a breeding population here. They must have eaten a lot of turkey. The wild turkey is now a rare bird on the island, and has become much more secretive and cautious. I rarely hear the loud gobble of a tom, or see a hen disappear into the forest with an entourage of poults, as baby turkeys are called. I for one am glad to have the turkey population under control, since one of their favorite foods is the fruit of Japanese barberry, a thorny invasive bush that thrives here. The turkeys probably unwittingly planted barberry seeds all over the island.

Turkeys are native to North America. Before the European settlement, wild turkeys ranged through much of eastern and central North America, north to the Great Lakes and southern Maine, and south into much of Mexico. Mayan and Aztec peoples domesticated the turkey, as did the Anasazi and Navajo peoples of the southwest. Spanish explorers encountered domesticated turkeys in Mexico in the 1500s and took them back to Europe. The domesticated turkey spread quickly over the European continent. It was mistakenly named "turkey" because much European trade in the 1500s was routed through Turkey and the bird became confused with peacocks and guinea fowl, which came from the east and were known as "Turkey cocks."

A hundred years later, when Europeans came to America to settle, they brought domesticated turkeys back with them. The pilgrims carried turkeys on the Mayflower, returning them to the land of their origin. European settlers introduced turkeys to many areas where they did not originally live—such as northern Maine.

By the mid-1800s, hunting and deforestation had eradicated wild turkeys from much of their range. At its nadir, the wild turkey population was only about 30,000 birds. Successful reintroduction efforts began in the 1940s, and wild turkey populations are now established in all the lower 48 States, a much larger range than that of the wild turkey before European settlement of America. Today the wild turkey population in North America is about 6.5 million.

Wild turkeys are large, gregarious game birds. Toms average about eighteen pounds and four feet long, while hens average only eight pounds and three feet long. During the winter turkeys wander their habitat of open woodlands and forests in large, single sex groups. They are omnivorous, foraging during the day on acorns and other nuts, wild fruits, seeds, ferns, insects, worms, salamanders, slugs, and snakes. They roost in trees at night.

In early spring the turkey mating season begins. Toms in pairs or small groups seek out flocks of hens, gobbling loudly to attract them. Dominant males display for the hens, strutting, puffing their feathers, spreading their tails high and wide, and dragging their wings as they turn about to show themselves from all angles. When a tom is excited, the skin on his naked head turns brilliant red, blue and white, and he makes loud thumping sounds followed by a low, vibrant hum. One dominant male may mate with many females.

Once mating has occurred, females disperse to find nest sites, choosing protected spots on the ground. A hen's ability to hide the nest is crucial. She makes a shallow depression, often in underbrush at the base of a tree. The hen lays one egg a day for 10 to 14 days. She begins the four-week incubation after the entire clutch has been laid. During this six-week period the nest is vulnerable to many predators. Raccoons, coyotes, foxes, skunks, red squirrels, crows, and snakes often discover and eat turkey eggs. A hen who loses her clutch of eggs to a predator early in the summer sometimes re-nests, which is why hens with young poults can sometimes be seen in August and September.

When the poults hatch they are fully feathered and able to walk. They leave the nest within 12 to 24 hours. Their mother quickly teaches them to forage, and she protects them under her wings from rain and cold. In their first few weeks poults often succumb to raccoons, foxes, coyotes, mink, weasels, hawks, owls, eagles—the dangers are legion. Turkeys are fast runners, and despite being strong flyers over short distances, they often run from predators rather than flying. The well-camouflaged poults scatter to confuse the pursuit. Even so, probably 60-80% of poults fall victim to predators. At one month old, poults are able to fly into trees to roost, and are increasingly fast, savvy, and safe. Coyotes are probably the most fearful predators of adult turkeys, as our experience on Isle au Haut suggests.

The domesticated turkeys we eat on Thanksgiving have been selectively bred to be much heavier and less active than their wild relatives, but they are the same species. They are unable to fly or run fast because of their great weight. Their feathers are usually white, and their breasts are much meatier and broader than wild turkey breasts. They are docile and take well to captivity. As I look back on the recent history of turkeys on Isle au Haut, I realize that they arrived in a place without foxes, coyotes, raccoons or skunks, and as a result became less and less wild over the years. It took the coyotes to make them truly wild again.

Common Garter Snakes
(Thamnophis sirtalis)

When I walk along a paved road in October, I often find a garter snake that has been killed by a passing car. I pick up the stiff, flattened body that was once so lithe and swift and secretive, and toss it aside to save it from the further indignity of tires and prying eyes. Snakes come out on the roads in autumn to bask in the weakening sun and soak up heat from the warm asphalt, little knowing that death awaits them there.

Snakes are ectotherms, which means that their body temperature is determined by their surroundings. I learned as a child that reptiles, amphibians, insects, and many other animals are "cold-blooded," but this is a misnomer. Terrestrial ectotherms actively regulate their body temperature by moving into warmer or cooler places. When too cool, they become sluggish and need to warm up. Turtles basking on logs, butterflies sitting in the sun with their wings spread, and snakes lying on rocks (or on the road), are warming their bodies so they can move about actively, and swim, fly, or hunt efficiently. These same animals, when too hot, will seek shade. A garter snake's ideal body temperature is in the mid 80s Fahrenheit.

Common garter snakes occur throughout much of North America. They adapt to many different habitats—marshes, fields, gardens, and forests—often near water. There is geographic variation in color and pattern, but garter snakes usually have a broad, dark head; three yellowish stripes running lengthwise down the body; a checkerboard of spots along the stripes; and a pale belly. They grow up to three feet long. Males are generally smaller than females, but with longer tails. (A snake's tail is the portion of the body behind the anus, or vent.)

Garter snakes are active during the day. They are good swimmers, and hunt in the water as well as on land. They prey on frogs and toads, earthworms, tadpoles, fish, insects, and even small rodents. Snakes' olfactory organs are located on their tongues, which constantly flick in and out as they try to locate and approach prey. The predators of garter snakes are primarily birds—hawks, crows, and great blue herons—as well as raccoons, minks, bullfrogs, snapping turtles, and other snakes.

Throughout the summer garter snakes are solitary animals, but in late October they travel as far as three miles to congregate below the frost line in large, communal dens called hibernacula. A hibernaculum is used year after year by garter snakes who winter there in suspended animation. Hundreds of snakes coil together in tight balls to conserve heat. On warm winter days, some may emerge from the den briefly to bask in the weak sunshine.

As the hibernaculum warms up in the spring, garter snakes awaken and emerge. Males come out first and wait for the emergence of the females. Each emerging female produces powerful pheromones that attract many males. Often a female is engulfed by a mating ball of up to twenty-five suitors. During mating the male transfers a packet of sperm called a spermatophore into the female. After mating, the female can save the spermatophore for many months. She uses it to fertilize her eggs once she has established a suitable hunting territory. She carries up to eighty fertilized eggs for two or three months. In late summer they hatch inside her body into baby snakes five to nine inches long. At this point, she gives birth to live young. The average litter of garter snakes is about twenty-five babies. No wonder the females are larger than the males!

Baby garter snakes are independent from birth, and must hunt aggressively throughout the fall to fatten up for their winter sleep. They find a hibernaculum by following trails of pheromones laid down by adult garter snakes. Many young snakes die before they reach sexual maturity at two or three years. If they survive their first year, garter snakes may live three or four years or more in the wild.

I wonder where the garter snakes of Isle au Haut spend their winters. I like to imagine their mysterious journeys to their winter dens. There are probably several hibernacula on the island, hidden deep under rocks. In many parts of the country, collectors wait at known hibernacula and gather garter snakes for the pet trade as they emerge in the spring. In some places, because of this practice, common garter snakes are becoming rare. Perhaps it is better that the garter snakes keep their secrets, and that we humans carry on with our busy lives.

Apples
(Malus domestica)

The Isle au Haut summer folks are gone. The road, lined with scarlet huckleberry bushes and overhung by brilliant maples, is almost empty of traffic. The houses in the village are mostly dark at night. Groups of deer in their gray winter coats graze openly on lawns. Many summer gardens are left to go to seed. Often, a summer friend will say to me, on leaving, "Please, feel free to harvest the last of my tomatoes, (or grapes, or blackberries, or parsley)." But the great bonanza of early October on Isle au Haut is apples.

It seems that just about every old home has its old apple trees. There must be many heirloom varieties here, but history has swallowed up their names. When I go to harvest apples, I move from tree to tree, tasting. Usually the deer have already taken most of the apples on the lower branches. So I scramble up into the crown, get a good foothold, and shake like mad. The falling apples make satisfying thumps hitting the ground. I come down to fill a bucket with the best of the fallen fruit, leaving the rest for the deer. A few bucketfuls make sauce for a year, sauce that is infused with memories of the crisp weather, the damp ground, the laden trees of early October.

The apple is an unusual tree. In most of the plant world if you sow a seed, you get a plant like the one the seed came from. Not so with apples. Every apple seed, even each seed in a single fruit, has genetic instructions for a new and different apple tree. If you sow an orchard from apple seeds, your trees will produce a medley of fruits of different sizes, shapes, colors, and tastes. That is why the seedling trees you buy in the nursery are all grafted onto apple rootstock. The only way to cultivate the kind of apple you want is to cut a scion branch from its tree, and graft it onto an apple root.

The wild ancestors of our apple trees grow in the forests of Kazakhstan in central Asia, where they produce a riotous array of apples. After the Chinese developed grafting techniques more than four thousand years ago, the apple spread around the world. In each climate zone different varieties were developed. Most of the apple trees the European settlers brought to New England could not survive the rigors of the American climate. But the settlers also planted apple seeds. John Chapman, aka Johnny Appleseed, brought apple seeds to the frontier, planting orchards, which produced apples for cider—the only source of alcoholic beverage available to the settlers. The settlers could make cider from just about any apple, but in each orchard, there might have been one tree that produced a sweet, delectable fruit. If the orchardist chose to propagate that tree by grafting, a new variety of American apple was born. Thus the apple, in early American history, provided liquor and also sweetness. In the days before honeybees and sugarcane were introduced to North America, sweetness was in short supply.

My yearly autumn excursion to gather apples on Isle au Haut is a kind of windfall. The oncoming loneliness of winter is offset by the generosity of both the trees and their owners. The applesauce I freeze and the pies we enjoy are reminders of the bounty of summer and of the summer friends who enrich our lives on the island.

Northern Flickers
(Colaptes auratus)

From the end of September through October, migrating flickers are everywhere on Isle au Haut. Their white rumps flash as they scatter in alarm from the roadsides before my oncoming car. Their loud calls distract me from my chores as I put my garden to bed. They rustle in the bushes and feed on the lawn. Every autumn I enjoy their presence as they make their way south for the winter.

The northern flicker is a species of woodpecker. The woodpeckers are a family of birds that includes about 200 species worldwide. Woodpeckers are distinguished by a number of special adaptations that enable them to drum loudly and rapidly on trees. Many of their feeding, breeding, and communication behaviors depend on this activity, which puts enormous stresses on their skulls, brains, and eyes.

Woodpeckers have strong, chisel-like bills. Powerful neck muscles enable woodpeckers to strike twenty or more times per second while drumming with tremendous force. A human brain subjected to a blow less forceful than one woodpecker strike would sustain a concussion. Woodpeckers avoid concussion because their brains are tightly fitted into skulls whose bones have a spongy, shock absorbing structure. Special membranes cover woodpeckers' eyes when they are drilling, holding the eyes in place and protecting them from flying debris. A layer of tiny feathers shields the woodpeckers' slit-shaped nostrils. Designers of helmets used to protect human skulls in sports and other activities study woodpecker skulls for new ideas.

Woodpeckers have several adaptations for maintaining a secure drumming posture on a vertical tree trunk. Their central tail feathers are stiffened, providing a prop to stabilize the body against the tree. Their legs are short and sturdy, and the four toes are arranged with two in front and two behind, allowing the woodpecker to grip the bark of the tree firmly when drilling and feeding. Woodpeckers have long, sticky tongues armed with bristles for extracting insect prey from the holes they drill. Woodpecker tongues, like those of hummingbirds, are often two or three times the length of the bill, and are coiled in the skull when not in use.

The northern flicker is a foot-long, brown woodpecker, speckled with black. It sports a red crescent on the back of its neck, a black collar, and a conspicuous white rump patch. Males have black whisker-marks at the sides of their bills. When I began watching birds in the 1960s the northern flicker was divided into two species, the western red-shafted flicker and the eastern yellow-shafted flicker. They were distinguished by the color of the central shafts and undersides of their wing feathers. Since 1973 flickers have been reclassified as a single species with several different races.

Flicker flight is typical of woodpeckers—a series of rapid wingbeats followed by a glide with wings folded against the body. This creates a distinctive undulating flight path. The flicker's call is a long series of loud "wik-wik-wik-wik" notes audible over a large area, and repeated many times a day during the nesting season.

Northern flickers range throughout North America. Flickers prefer open woodlands and forest edges, and are often found in parks and suburbs. Like all woodpeckers, flickers' preferred food is insects, particularly ants and beetles. They also eat berries and seeds, especially in the winter. But unlike most woodpeckers, flickers forage on the ground, hunting for ants and grubs. They hammer into the soil with their strong beaks, lapping up insects and larvae with their long, barbed tongues. This ground feeding habit is what makes flickers so prominent in the fall as they feed along the mowed edges of roads and startle up, their white rumps conspicuous in flight, when cars pass.

Most woodpeckers stay put all year. Flickers, however, are strongly migratory in the northern part of their range. They move south in loose flocks in the autumn and spend the winters dispersed throughout the southern United States.

In early spring flickers form flocks again and return north. Male birds arrive first, often returning to the same areas where they have nested before. They establish territories by drumming loudly on resonant objects. Hollow trees, gutters, and transformers on telephone poles all serve as flicker drumming platforms. One spring when I was living in a cabin in the woods of New Hampshire, a flicker chose the kerosene tank outside my bedroom window as his early morning display post. He drove me crazy. Like all woodpeckers, flickers drum instead of singing in order to proclaim their territorial imperative. They also give their loud, ringing "wik-wik-wik-wik" call. During the establishment of territories flickers engage in elaborate courtship displays.

Once the pair bond is formed, the couple works together for a week or more to excavate a cavity more than a foot deep in a dead or diseased tree. The cavity is wider at the bottom and lined with a bed of wood chips. Sometimes flickers reuse or repair an existing cavity, working to make it larger, cleaner, and more comfortable. Cavities are in demand by many species, and the flickers must actively guard their nest holes from seizure by other birds.

The female lays five to eight white eggs. The parents take turns incubating the eggs for eleven or twelve days. Young flickers hatch naked and helpless, with eyes sealed shut. For four days the parents must take turns constantly brooding the chicks to regulate their temperature. Once the chicks have developed their downy feathers they can stay in the nest while their parents forage for food. The parents feed their chicks by regurgitating nutritious insect prey.

At three weeks old, the young have feathered out and can cling to the cavity walls and stick their heads out the entrance hole as they beg for food. The little wooden room that serves as the flicker family's house must feel awfully crowded as the babies grow big. At four weeks the chicks fledge, leaving the cavity forever. They continue to depend on their parents for food, following the adults to foraging sites where they learn to hunt for themselves.

The flickers passing through Isle au Haut in the autumn are quieter than they were last spring. They have no need for territorial drumming or loud calls. Instead they are moving in flocks, pausing during the day to put on fat for the journey, and migrating at night. I often hear their single, clear contact note—"kyeer!"—which they use to keep track of flock-mates as they feed. This drawing together of many individuals in migratory flocks after the summer of territorial wrangling and reproductive activity seems a peaceful, companionable conclusion to the busy summer season. I often find myself leaning on my garden fork, taking a moment to rest and enjoy their passage.

Periwinkles

(Littorina littorea, Littorina obtusata, Littorina saxatilis)

When I explore the intertidal zone along the rocky coast of Isle au Haut, some of the rocks are literally covered with snails. These are common periwinkles, our most abundant intertidal snail. There are so many of them that it boggles the mind to imagine the numbers that thrive from Delaware up the Atlantic coast to Labrador. Surprisingly, the common periwinkle is an invasive species. It arrived from Europe, probably in the 1840s, in ships' ballast. Scientists believe that the arrival of the common periwinkle fundamentally changed our intertidal ecology by displacing native snails and changing the distribution of seaweeds. People who walked our shoreline in 1800 would have seen a lush green carpet of algae covering the rocks instead of the bare, grey rocks we see today. Common periwinkles grazing the rocky shore made the difference.

Photo by John DeWitt

We have three species of periwinkles in coastal Maine: the common periwinkle, the smooth periwinkle, and the rough periwinkle. Common periwinkles are familiar to anyone who has wandered the tidepools, rocks, and cobbles along the shore. They live throughout the intertidal zone, preferring areas where they are submerged in water for at least part of each day. Smooth periwinkles live in seaweeds in the lower intertidal zone. They have flat-tipped shells and come in a variety of colors from brown to bright yellow to banded. Rough periwinkles colonize the rocks in the high intertidal zone. They are grey and slightly ridged, and because they live on rocks that are covered only by the highest tides, they have developed the ability to breathe air. Both smooth and rough periwinkles are smaller and less abundant than common periwinkles, and were here before the European settlement of North America.

Common periwinkles have dark, thick spiral shells and grow to about an inch long. They live to be five to ten years old. They are grazers, eating primarily the algal film that grows on the rocks. Each snail is equipped with a file-like radula, which it uses to scrape algae from the rock surface. It digests the algae by mixing it with mucous secreted onto the radula before it brings the food into its mouth. In areas where periwinkles are abundant the rocks are continually scraped clean of algae. Though each periwinkle is small, over time the combined action of all their radulae can erode the rocks where they feed.

Common periwinkles live in a wide variety of environmental conditions including extreme heat and cold, pounding surf, strong winds, and long periods of exposure to air. Some live below the intertidal, continually submerged. Others frequent the upper intertidal, and are only occasionally underwater. Most prefer areas where the tide covers and uncovers them daily. Periwinkles are equipped with a tight-fitting operculum, a hard plate that fits exactly into the shell's opening and protects the snail from predators and from drying out. A periwinkle breathes with gills but can survive for many days above the tideline by retracting into its shell, sealed in by its operculum. It secretes a cement-like mucous that secures it firmly to the rock. When it is ready to feed, the periwinkle breaks the seal from inside its shell and moves along. Periwinkles move on a muscular foot that is separated into two halves. Each half moves ahead alternately, carrying the snail forward. A periwinkle's sensory organs are on their forked tentacles, which contain rudimentary eyes as well as organs of touch and taste.

The periwinkle's most dangerous predator is the sea star. A periwinkle's strong shell and tightly-fitting operculum are no match for a sea star, which wraps its arms around the periwinkle and engulfs it. The periwinkle's best defense is to live above the low tide line, since sea stars cannot survive prolonged exposure to air.

Human beings also prey on periwinkles. Since prehistoric times, people have gathered them for food. In Scotland and Ireland, gathering periwinkles is an eight million dollar per year business, peaking at Christmastime when periwinkles are in demand in France. Here on Isle au Haut periwinkles occasionally show up at pot-luck suppers steamed in saltwater and served with melted butter and toothpicks for extracting them from their shells.

Periwinkles mate periodically throughout the year, but each of our three periwinkle species has a different reproductive strategy. Smooth periwinkles, which live on rockweed, mate and lay their eggs on the seaweed. The eggs hatch into mini-adult snails that eat the seaweed where they hatched. Rough periwinkles live in drier conditions. After mating, the female keeps her eggs inside her body until they hatch into tiny snails, which then leave their mother and start life on their own on the rocks.

Common periwinkles mate, and then wait to release their eggs into the sea until the high tides that occur just after the new or full moon. The females release egg capsules containing three to ten eggs each. A large female may produce 100,000 eggs per year. The egg capsules float away into the plankton, where they hatch into swimming larvae that look nothing like adult snails. The larvae, carried by tides and currents, feed and grow in the plankton for two to four weeks, transform into tiny snails, and settle to the bottom to find permanent homes. Because of their planktonic beginnings, periwinkles can spread rapidly. This adaptation facilitated the periwinkles' invasion of our Atlantic coast after their accidental introduction more than 150 years ago.

What a difference 150 years can make in an ecosystem! Invasive species, which are usually transported from their native habitat by human beings, can change the ecology of a place in a remarkably short period of time. If an introduced species arrived long ago, we think of it as characteristic of our local habitats, and look on its members with fondness and familiarity—as I do with periwinkles. But habitats are always changing, and some of our most common species, like the common periwinkle, are actually colonists from other worlds. Like the Europeans who brought them, periwinkles have altered their environment to a point where it is unrecognizable as the same place it was when they arrived.

Bird Migration

At the beginning of autumn there are still hummingbirds coming to the petunias on my deck and crowds of young goldfinches emptying my bird feeders. Sharp-shinned hawks are preying on the feeder birds, and flocks of cormorants scrawl their wavering vees across the sky. Flickers that have been feeding by the roadsides fly up, their white rumps retreating ahead of my car. All of these birds are readying themselves for the dangerous, taxing trip south to their wintering grounds. There are warblers in the trees, hawks in the skies, and shorebirds on the beaches. The fall migration is in full swing. It is always a bit sad to see our summer birds, many of them molted into somber winter colors, leaving our dooryards for more southerly climes.

Red-necked Phalaropes - Photo By Marnie Davis

We have all seen flocks of birds of various species departing our coast in the fall and arriving again in the spring. Despite the dangers and challenges of long journeys through unfamiliar territory, many species of birds migrate. What is it that draws them north every spring when they could easily stay in the warm places where they spend the winter?

Breeding in the north has many advantages for birds. In the tropics, where it is always warm, food sources and nesting sites are available constantly throughout the year. But there is not enough food or territory to accommodate the tropical resident birds as well as our migratory species during their breeding seasons. Here in the north there are numerous nesting territories available for spring arrivals. Food may be scarce in the winter but it is abundant in the spring and summer. There are great hatches of insects that provide a bountiful larder for foraging birds. Think black flies, mosquitoes, multitudes of caterpillars! They may be a bother to us, but they are essential for our songbirds. Summer days are long and full of light, allowing extra hours for finding food to pack into those gaping maws waiting in the nest. Many songbirds are able to raise two or even three broods in the northern summer sunshine.

When the nesting season is over, there is still a supply of food—both here and en route—to fatten the migrating flocks as they head south. Insects are plentiful, and nutritious seeds and berries add to the banquet. Migratory birds have physiological adaptations that enable them to take special advantage of this autumn bonanza of food, as well as many structural adaptations that make their taxing long-distance journeys possible.

Migratory birds have internal clocks that respond to day length and weather. These internal clocks trigger big metabolic changes that cause birds to gain weight at extraordinary rates. Birds' appetites increase along with their ability to convert food to body fat. Before and during migration, a bird can gain ten percent of its body weight a day in fat. In the days before a long haul across mountains, a desert or an ocean, a songbird's weight might be as much as fifty percent fat, which is then used up in one arduous flight. Imagine if you weighed a hundred and fifty pounds, put on fifteen pounds a day until you weighed three hundred pounds, and then exercised continuously, losing two pounds an hour for seventy-five hours! A warbler migrating across the Gulf of Mexico does something like that. Once songbirds have reached their destinations, they return to their normal metabolism and normal eating habits.

The internal systems of a bird's body minimize weight during flight. Birds don't have bladders because it would be burdensome to carry around all that liquid. Instead, they concentrate their urine into uric acid—the white stuff you can see in bird droppings. The uric acid is deposited into the intestine, and the bird packages all its waste into one compact package before excreting it. Birds also digest food and concentrate their urine very quickly, thereby getting rid of the extra weight shortly after feeding.

Have you ever noticed how an eagle, gull, or heron often poops just as it takes off? It is jettisoning extra weight.

Because of their amazing exertions in flight, birds have the most efficient hearts and lungs in the animal kingdom. A bird's heart is six times the relative weight of a human heart and is built to stand up to the demands of long-distance flight. A resting goldfinch's heart beats about five hundred times per minute, and a hummingbird's heart a thousand times per minute. Our resting pulse rate is only sixty to a hundred beats per minute.

A bird's respiratory system occupies about twenty percent of its body space, while ours takes up only about five percent. Birds have air sacs surrounding their lungs. When a bird breathes in, air flows into these sacs instead of directly into the lungs. The sacs act like bellows, pumping a constant flow of fresh air through the lungs. When a mammal exhales, the lungs must wait for fresh oxygen until it inhales again. When a bird exhales, the air sacs continue to supply fresh air to the lungs. Birds' lungs never have to wait for oxygen.

Birds' skeletons are adapted to be light and strong. All their bones are riddled with air spaces. The long bones are hollow, strengthened by internal struts. The slender pelican wing bone I found once on a California beach is a foot long, but seems to weigh nothing in my hand. A bird's breastbone has a keel to anchor the muscles that drive the wings. The spine is fused to withstand the forces of flight.

Birds' feathers, like their bones, are a marvel of lightness and strength. Insulating down allows birds to regulate their temperatures and stay warm. Contour feathers cover the body, holding in warmth, affording protection from weather, and giving the bird its form and colors. The long, stiff flight feathers of the wings and tail generate both thrust and lift, endowing the bird with its ability to fly. Most birds molt before migration, shedding old feathers and growing new ones so that their feathers will be in good shape for the journey.

Despite the adaptations that prepare birds for migratory flight, they face numerous dangers on the way. Many die of exhaustion or starvation. Habitat destruction, especially in areas migratory birds have traditionally used for resting and refueling, can make it impossible for them to find enough food. Weakened, exhausted birds are less wary and more vulnerable to errors of judgment. Local predators, particularly outdoor pet cats and feral cats, kill hundreds of thousands of migratory songbirds every year. Collisions with buildings and other human-made structures also account for many songbird deaths. When I lived in Boston years ago, every morning during the spring migration a hired cleaner removed dead warblers off the street under the Hancock Tower, a glass skyscraper.

Many northern species have evolved behaviors and physical adaptations to avoid the dangers of migration. These species, like our familiar juncos and chickadees, stay in the north all winter. As I restock our feeders to help our resident birds through the oncoming darkness and cold, I watch our summer birds heading south. I think of their courage, their beauty, their strength, their lightness, and their energy efficient bodies. I also think of the hazards they face as they head for warmer places. I wish them safe passage, now, as they leave our coast, and again in the springtime as they migrate north for another breeding season.

Voles

(Microtus pennsylvanicus)

I have an ongoing war with voles. These little critters wreak havoc in my vegetable garden, and I can't seem to find a way to stop them. They particularly love my beans, carrots, beets, parsnips, Brussels sprouts, and potatoes. A case in point: one fall many years ago, as I was harvesting carrots and parsnips, I found that all I had left were the tops. The roots themselves had disappeared. Then I discovered, by accidentally stepping on a collapsing piece of garden earth, that the voles had constructed an underground storage facility for carrots and parsnips in my garden. They had stacked my veggies in neat piles in a sizeable root cellar, the way I stack firewood. The nerve! I took my carrots and parsnips back, cutting off the nibbled parts. Then I planned vengeance.

The first thing I tried was building a chicken yard around three sides of my vegetable garden, expecting that the voles would not be willing to cross the open ground created by the chickens. That helped a bit. I also use mousetraps in the garden, but it is hard to go out night after night all summer long to set my traps, and then retrieve them early every morning. I am not willing to leave the traps out in the daytime because they catch songbirds. I have given up on raising bush beans, which I think of as vole magnets. I now plant only pole beans, whose stems I surround with high, vole-proof walls of rigid plastic. I've tried using the pellets sold in garden stores that supposedly repel voles. I can't tell whether or not they are effective. I am lucky to have a dog whose favorite activity is hunting voles, and she is frequently successful. But, in spite of everything I've tried, I continue to lose a lot of produce every year to voles.

Voles are small rodents, slightly larger and chunkier than field mice, with blunt noses, small ears, dark grey or brown fur, and short, hairless tails. They live under cover of dense vegetation where they find protection from predators. They prefer brushy areas and fields where they make little above-ground tunnels called runways extending outwards from their nests through the thick grass. They also use old burrows, stone walls, spaces under logs and boards, and any other form of cover near the ground's surface. Although their pathways are above ground, they are skillful diggers. They remain active in tunnels under the snow all winter. At snowmelt in the spring, you can often find mazes of their tunnels in last year's dead grass.

Voles eat mostly plants, enjoying succulent fresh vegetation in the summer, switching to seeds and bark in the winter. They can tunnel beneath the soil surface to eat bulbs, tubers, and roots. During the winter they often girdle fruit trees. Fruit tree owners in our neck of the woods are wise to protect the trunks with surrounds of rat wire to ward off hungry voles.

Female voles become sexually mature at less than a month old and proceed to have five or more litters a year with four to eight young per litter. That's a lot of voles. However, voles have very short life spans, usually less than a year, because they fall victim to so many different predators. On Isle au Haut, where we don't have foxes or raccoons, voles are prey for coyotes, owls, hawks, crows, herons, and snakes...and gardeners like me. I kill voles to protect my vegetables. Wild carnivores kill them for food. I am one more critter trying to feed myself. It is all a part of nature's balance. When I ask myself the hypothetical question, "If you could rid the earth of voles, would you do it?" the answer is no. Voles are an important part of the food web that sustains all the life around me. But I do wish I could keep them out of my garden.

Black-capped Chickadees
(Poecile atricapillus)

In the fall black-capped chickadees come together in small territorial flocks that will feed together all winter. If you walk in the woods or along the roads, you are likely to find a flock feeding actively in the trees, calling to each other as they move about in search of food. These tiny, energetic creatures are preparing to face the frigid temperatures, daunting storms, and long nights of the Maine winter. The summer songbirds have left the coast of Maine, choosing the dangers of a migratory journey over the dangers of prolonged cold and darkness. The small songbirds that remain—juncos, kinglets, nuthatches and chickadees chief among them—must manage to stay warm and find sufficient food to survive an entire season in conditions that could extinguish a human life in one night.

Photo by John DeWitt

The black-capped chickadee, Maine's state bird, is a common and cheerful presence all year. It lives throughout northern North America. With its black cap and bib, white cheeks, gray back, buffy sides, round head, and signature chickadee-dee-dee call, this little bird is unmistakable. Despite their small size, chickadees are long-lived; the oldest known wild chickadee was over twelve years old. Chickadees are curious and sociable—you can, with a little patience, get a chickadee to land on your hand if you stand quietly with a palm full of sunflower seeds. But since a chickadee weighs less than half an ounce—about the same as four pennies—you will feel mainly the scratch of tiny claws.

Chickadees mate for life. Unmated birds find partners in the feeding flocks that form in autumn. In late winter, males begin to sing their sweet two-note song, and the winter flocks break up. Chickadee pairs claim territories and, as spring arrives, excavate cavity nests in rotten snags, often birch. The female lays about eight eggs and incubates them for two weeks while the male brings her food. When the naked chicks hatch, the mother broods them until they grow downy feathers. Then both parents feed the quickly growing babies. The young leave the nest at about sixteen days but stay on the breeding territory for another month before heading off on their own. In the fall, chickadees gather again in small flocks that will stay together during the winter.

Chickadees eat insects, spiders, berries, and seeds. They feed by gleaning the foliage and bark of trees, often hanging acrobatically upside down on twigs. They come readily to feeders, and prefer nutritious black-oil sunflower seeds. As chickadees feed, they call to each other constantly. If you listen carefully you can hear many different vocalizations other than the familiar chickadee-dee-dee. All fall, chickadees stash food in various places—bark, dead leaves, knotholes, etc. A chickadee can remember hundreds of different locations and retrieve stored food as needed. Every year, in order to clear their brains for the new information they will need to remember, chickadees actually refresh their brains by allowing neurons that held old knowledge to die, replacing them with new neurons. Chickadees feed constantly through the short winter days. A feeding flock of chickadees is often joined by other species like kinglets and nuthatches, which depend on the chickadees for food location and warnings of danger.

Staying warm in winter is a huge challenge for a tiny creature like a chickadee. The smaller the animal, the greater the ratio of body surface area to body mass, and the more heat is lost. Chickadees are adapted to conserve heat and find enough food to fuel their tiny bodies. Except on the coldest nights, chickadees roost alone, tucking themselves into small cavities or dense foliage with their heads under their wings. They puff up their feathers to maximize the insulation of their tiny down coats. They constrict the blood vessels directly under their skins to reduce heat loss. On the coldest nights, chickadees may roost communally, taking advantage of the warmth of other bodies. Amazingly, a chickadee can lower its body temperature by as much as fourteen degrees from its normal temperature of 110 degrees, decreasing metabolic rate to conserve energy. This temporary lowering of body temperature, called torpor, is rare among birds.

As we close the windows, fire up the woodstove, and lay extra blankets on the bed, I think about what the night is like for the animals who face winter outdoors. The busy, exuberant activity of chickadees at the feeder and in the woods on winter days seems heroic to me. Their songs and calls sound light-hearted and optimistic. I know I am projecting my feelings onto them, but I wish that I could maintain such a positive attitude when the challenges of life seem overwhelming.

Grasshoppers
(*Caelifera* spp.)

During the fall in my garden I am often interrupted by large grasshoppers landing beside me. They are heavy—I can hear the impact of their bodies on the soil—and they seem confused and clumsy. They are probably near death. A friend told me that she has grasshoppers crawling all over her deck, laying their eggs between the decking boards. They are probably disoriented by the chilly nights, hurrying to lay their eggs somewhere before the cold arrives in earnest.

In June and early July small grasshoppers proliferate in my garden, hopping around on the plants, nimbly dodging to the far side of a leaf or grass blade at my approach. As the summer progresses, they grow bigger. Then in August another grasshopper species—a band-winged grasshopper—appears along dirt driveways, rocky trails, and in dry, open, areas with sparse grass. Band-winged grasshoppers are inconspicuous on the ground but when alarmed they leap into the air and fly off, flaring vividly striped black and white wings, clicking them together loudly. That clicking sound startles me every summer. It always takes me a breathless second to remember that there are no rattlesnakes on Isle au Haut.

There are 630 species of grasshoppers in North America. Grasshoppers are members of the insect order Orthoptera, which also includes crickets and katydids. All Orthopterans have wings, large compound eyes, and long hind legs for jumping. They are mainly herbivorous, and most species will eat many different kinds of plants. Some also scavenge dead insects or take live prey. Most use sound in their courtship rituals, clicking their wings against each other, which is called crepitation, or rubbing their wings or legs together, which is called stridulation. Crickets, whose chirping chorus graces our fields in the fall, are stridulating to attract mates.

Grasshoppers, like all insects, have three body parts—the head, the thorax, and the abdomen. The head contains the jaws, called mandibles, which are exceptionally strong and adapted for chewing plant tissue. There are two large compound eyes, each with thousands of individual lenses. Each of these lenses faces a slightly different direction and sends an image to the brain, which assembles the images into a full picture of the grasshopper's surroundings. There are also three simple eyes on top of the head between the compound eyes. I like to imagine being able to see in all directions at once, like a grasshopper.

The thorax is where a grasshopper's legs and wings are attached. The three pairs of legs are used for walking, a grasshopper's main method of locomotion. But the hindmost pair of legs is long and strong. This pair functions like a miniature catapult, enabling the grasshopper to jump twenty times the length of its body or to fling itself into flight. The grasshopper's abdomen contains many of its organs including its ears, which are membranes tucked under the wings.

Insects are divided into two groups based on their life cycle. The larger group undergoes a developmental process called complete metamorphosis with four stages, each completely different from the others. The first stage is the egg. The egg hatches into a larva—caterpillar, maggot, or grub—which eats, grows, and transforms into a pupa. Inside the pupa, the contents of the body dissolve and reorganize into the adult form. The adult hatches out of the pupa, mates, and lays eggs to begin the cycle again. Beetles, butterflies, ants, bees, wasps, and many other insects undergo complete metamorphosis.

Grasshoppers are part of the smaller group of insects whose life cycle is called incomplete metamorphosis. These insects begin as eggs and hatch into nymphs, which are tiny but incomplete replicas of their parents. A nymph eats and grows, molting its exoskeleton as it gets bigger. The period between molts is called an instar. In each instar the nymph gains more adult characteristics, such as wings and coloration. In the final molt, it develops complete genitalia, becoming a sexually mature adult, ready to mate, lay eggs and start the cycle again. Some examples of insects that undergo incomplete metamorphosis are grasshoppers, crickets, cockroaches, termites, true bugs, and praying mantises.

Grasshopper eggs hatch in the spring. The nymphs go through five instars, all of which look like small adult grasshoppers. This is why insects like grasshoppers appear in many different sizes throughout the summer. You will never see tiny monarch butterflies, or different sizes of ladybugs. Butterflies and beetles undergo complete metamorphosis and emerge fully-grown. But if you look carefully, you are sure to observe many sizes of grasshoppers, cockroaches, or crickets.

By the middle of the summer grasshoppers have attained sexual maturity. Depending on what species it is, a male grasshopper may stridulate (chirp) or crepitate (click) to attract a female. Duly impressed, the female approaches the male. The pair may engage in elaborate posturing before they mate. As they mate the male deposits a spermatophore, or packet of sperm, in a receptacle in the female's abdomen. When she is ready she uses the spermatophore to fertilize her eggs. She inserts her ovipositor, a special tubular organ at the end of her abdomen, into the ground, and lays her rice-shaped eggs an inch or two deep. She doesn't lay all her eggs at one time or in one place. Rather, she lays as many as ten batches, with ten to several hundred eggs per batch. She coats each batch with a sticky substance that hardens underground, encasing the eggs in a pod. The eggs overwinter underground in their pod and hatch into tiny nymphs when the weather warms in the spring. Adult grasshoppers die when cold weather arrives. They have lived about a year, nine months as an egg and three months as an active insect.

Grasshoppers and humans have a long history together. Grasshoppers can be fearsome agricultural pests. Locusts are actually grasshoppers that have formed swarms. In some conditions, grasshoppers multiply rapidly and become so numerous that they exhaust available food sources and join migratory swarms that fly over the landscape eating all the vegetation in their path. This can cause catastrophic damage to crops, with huge regional economic and social impacts. Abundant grasshoppers are also an important food source in many human cultures worldwide. But grasshoppers don't swarm in Maine, and I don't eat them. In my garden they are only slightly damaging, eating holes in the leaves of my veggies. I'm happy to coexist with grasshoppers.

Woolly Bear Caterpillars
(Pyrrharctia isabella)

Every time I go out into my yard and garden in October, I encounter woolly bear caterpillars on the move. They are easy to spot as they trundle along, rippling purposefully across the driveway, through the grass, even up the side of the chicken house. I often move them out of harm's way. When I pick up a woolly bear, it curls defensively into a ball to protect its soft belly, and I can feel its stiff bristles against my hand. I set it into tall grass or underbrush, and hope it will make its way to wherever it is trying to go. Why do woolly bears suddenly appear in the autumn, and where are they going?

Photo by John DeWitt

The woolly bear is an insect, the larval form of the Isabella tiger moth, a common moth that lives throughout North America. These night-flying moths are attracted to light, and you can often see them on your window screens at night during the summer. The moth is a nondescript tannish yellow with scattered black spots on its wings. Like most moths, it has a furry body and feather-like antennae, and it rests with its wings spread rather than folded.

Nocturnal insects must use senses other than sight to find their mates. The Isabella tiger moth uses smell. These moths live only a week or two and must find mates quickly. The female chooses a perch and extends a scent gland from the tip of her abdomen, broadcasting her perfume into the wind. Males zigzag through the night air trying to detect a female's pheromone by using receptors on their feathery antennae. When a male picks up the desirable scent, he follows it to the female and mates with her. Then he departs to seek other females while she flies off to lay her eggs on a variety of host plants. She lays her eggs under cover of darkness, distributing them widely.

The fuzzy caterpillar we call a woolly bear hatches from its egg after about a week. It is hungry, and immediately starts to eat and grow. At this early stage, the tiny woolly bear can relocate to new food plants by spinning out a thread of silk. Using this silken line, it floats into the breeze or tightropes to another plant to find food. Woolly bears are generalists, which means they feed on many different plants including grasses, asters, birches, clovers, maples, sunflowers, and many others.

As the woolly bear eats and grows it must molt, or shed its skin, many times. All creatures with exoskeletons—insects, crustaceans, spiders, etc.—have outer coverings that serve as the support structure for their bodies. They cannot grow without molting their old skins or shells and emerging in new, larger skins. The stage between molts is called an instar, and the woolly bear has five to seven instars, entering a new instar each time it sheds. The newly hatched woolly bear is mostly black with a brownish red band across the middle. It has thirteen body segments. Each time it sheds, another segment turns brown. So, as the woolly bear grows, the brown band gets wider. A woolly bear that has been feeding for a long time goes through more molts and has a wider brown band.

Many of us know the legend that you can predict the severity of the coming winter by noting the width of the brown band on the woolly bear—the wider the brown band, the milder the coming winter. It is true that the width of the brown band depends on weather-related conditions. An early spring or a long fall allows caterpillars to hatch earlier and/or feed later in the season. A wide brown band tells us of a milder than usual spring, summer, and fall in the past year. It is telling us about past rather than future weather.

We don't notice woolly bears throughout the summer because they feed at night. But when fall arrives, woolly bears venture out in the daytime to look for places to spend the winter in hiding, usually under the leaf litter or in dense vegetation. That is why we find so many woolly bears crawling about in October. When winter comes, a woolly bear freezes solid. Its heart stops beating, and it is apparently lifeless, a state called diapause that lasts throughout the winter. With the advent of spring's warmer temperatures, each woolly bear thaws and awakens, feeds for a short time, and prepares for its transformation into a moth.

The woolly bear spins a soft cocoon on the ground using its body hairs woven together with silk. Inside the cocoon the caterpillar sheds its skin for the last time. It is now a pupa. It hardens into a reddish, bean-shaped chrysalis inside the cocoon. Its caterpillar body dissolves into a liquid. In the liquid are small clusters of cells called imaginal disks, which are somewhat like stem cells. These imaginal disks were formed in the caterpillar and became active at the very end of the caterpillar's growth. Once the caterpillar has changed into a pupa, the imaginal disks grow and differentiate rapidly into the various organs of the moth—wings, eyes, legs, and internal organs. In a couple of weeks the new Isabella tiger moth hatches, chews its way out of its cocoon, inflates its wings, and flies away. It will never eat again. It has only a short time to find a mate and reproduce before it dies.

All around us insects are preparing for winter. Most of them are invisible to us. But we can see the woolly bear. The plucky caterpillars muscling through the grass, trekking across the flowerbeds, and braving expanses of gravel driveway are inspiring in a modest way. Good luck, little woolly bears! I hope to see you in the spring transformed into Isabella tiger moths on my window screens.

Fall Colors

Walking the roads and trails of Isle au Haut in the crisp fall weather is a pleasure tinged with sadness. The low autumn sunshine lights the leaves sidewise, making them shine. The red maples blaze, the birches flutter yellow in the wind, the huckleberries show deep red under the pitch pines, the oaks turn russet. The spruce trees that usually dominate the landscape seem to stand aside for the other trees, which step forward in all their glory.

What causes this amazing change in the colors of leaves? The deep green of summer leaves is produced by the pigment chlorophyll. Chlorophyll, which is found in all green plants, is the molecule that activates photosynthesis, the process by which plants capture light energy from the sun and transform it into chemical energy. This chemical energy is then used to manufacture simple sugars and oxygen from water and carbon dioxide. Chlorophyll makes this transformation happen. The Greek word photosynthesis means, literally, "putting together with light." Without chlorophyll most life on earth would be impossible. There would be no plants and no animals, because all animals rely directly or indirectly on plants for their food. In midsummer, leaves are busy making food in the long hours of sunshine, and chlorophyll is the dominant pigment.

The powerful color of chlorophyll conceals the presence of other pigments in the leaves. Many leaves are also rich in carotenoids, which are the yellow and orange pigments that give carrots, bananas, corn, daffodils, buttercups and many other plants their colors. In autumn, as the days grow shorter, trees respond by shutting down the production of chlorophyll. Leaves are vulnerable to damage by frost, and the tree needs to jettison its leaves to prepare for the dormancy of winter. As the chlorophyll dies away, the yellows and oranges that have been hidden under the green are unmasked, and the leaves change color. Meanwhile, the tree reabsorbs some of the nutrients held in the leaves. Once the tree has reclaimed as much as possible from the leaves, it weakens the attachment of the leaves to the stems. In some trees, particularly maples with their sweet sap, sugar is trapped in the leaves as the leaf-to-stem connection breaks down. When these sugary leaves are exposed to bright sunlight, they produce anthocyanins, the pigments that cause the brilliant scarlets and oranges which light up our forests in autumn. Then the leaves begin to fall, filling the air and carpeting the earth with their colors.

Soon I will be walking down roads looking at bare branches against the sky. With the leaves mostly fallen now, I still enjoy scuffing through them, kicking them up ahead of me, listening to them rustle. After the next hard rains, the leaves will be sodden and deteriorating underfoot. While the trees burn with autumn colors it seems that this last flare of beauty must be designed to lift the human spirit. But really, it is the expression of a process of change whose next phase is the falling of leaves. For the forest, this is a crucial part of the cycle of life. The leaves are proceeding with the real work they still have to do. They are decomposing and adding their sustenance to the poor soils of our rockbound island, providing next summer's nourishment for the trees that gave the leaves life in the first place.

Great Blue Herons
(Ardea herodias)

One of the sad things about autumn for me is that I can't be sure when I have seen the last of something. In spring I can welcome the first red-winged blackbird or the first flowers on the red maples or the first worm castings on the thawing earth. In autumn, when various life forms are migrating away or dying off or going into suspended animation, there is only a sense of diminution. I am pretty sure that this week I saw the last great blue heron of the season. I hadn't seen one for a couple of weeks. The weather is getting cold and the leaves are mostly off the trees. There was one solitary heron standing on the bleak edge of a cattail marsh.

Photo by Joan Handel

Great blue herons are the largest North American herons, living all over the continent. They stand a majestic four feet tall with a six-foot wingspan. Despite their great size they weigh only five or six pounds because, like most other birds, they have hollow bones. They are blue-gray overall, with broad black stripes over the eyes and a white crown. The chest appears shaggy, with long, fraying feathers that grow continually. The heron combs these feathers with its bill, and the powdery fragments it combs away remove fish slime and marsh oils from its breast.

Males and females are similar in appearance, with long, sinuous necks, long slender legs, and dagger-like bills for spearing prey. The great blue heron has specially adapted cervical vertebrae that enable it to fold its neck into an S-curve, allowing it to strike prey quickly from a distance and to shorten its flight profile for greater aerodynamic efficiency. When a heron takes flight it leaps into the air, often with a harsh croak, sometimes ejecting feces to decrease its flight load. Shortly after taking off the heron folds its neck. In flight the head is tucked back, the wingbeats are slow and deep, and the long legs trail behind.

Great blue herons are carnivores. They will eat just about anything they can catch, though they specialize in fish. They hunt in both fresh and saltwater wetlands and along shorelines. They may stand stock still peering into the water or stalk with infinitesimal slowness through the shallows, looking for aquatic prey. They also forage in grassy meadows for mice, voles, and insects. A great blue heron stalking is a picture of total concentration. The heron strikes with a lightning-quick stab of its long bill, often orienting the prey to face headfirst down its esophagus, sometimes tossing a fish in the air to position it correctly for its trip down the long throat.

Great blue herons nest in colonies, usually high in tall trees near water. A colony may have hundreds of nests, but also may be much smaller. Males arrive at the nesting grounds first, each aggressively claiming an existing nest or a place for a new nest. The male defends his nesting spot fiercely, even though nest sites are close together. Females arrive shortly after the males. Both sexes are in breeding plumage, with elegant, long plumes adorning their heads, throats and backs. Herons are monogamous during each mating season, but choose new mates each year. The males display for the females, performing circular flights with slow, exaggerated wingbeats and fully extended necks. They also display from the nest site, stretching their necks high into the air while bristling their plumes. Initially the male's level of territorial aggression may be so high that he drives away interested females, but eventually his aggression calms and he signals his readiness for pair bonding by offering his intended a stick, which she accepts and uses in construction of the nest. Nests in heron rookeries begin as flimsy platforms, but become massive over many years of use.

The female builds or fortifies the nest using sticks foraged for her by the male. When she is satisfied with the platform, she weaves a nest cup of grass, pine needles, and other soft materials in the center of the platform. Herons mate on their nests, and the female stores the male's sperm in her oviducts to fertilize each egg as it is laid. She lays three to five blue eggs about three inches long, one every two to three days, but begins incubating when the first egg is laid. This means that the eggs hatch sequentially, with the first chick hatched having an advantage for survival, especially in lean years. The parents take turns incubating until all the eggs have hatched, about 28 days for each egg. The babies hatch as downy chicks with their eyes open, unable to stand or to regulate their body temperature. But they are ready to be fed. The chicks grow quickly. At two weeks old they are six inches long; by four weeks, they have grown to a foot long; and at six weeks they have attained their adult size—about four feet tall. It is hard to imagine how many fish the parents need to provide to feed three to five babies who grow that fast.

As the chicks grow, the nest gets very crowded. The young herons stand on the nest platform exercising their wings, squabbling with each other, and vocalizing as they wait for their parents to arrive with food. Multiply all this activity by a hundred or more nearby nests, many in the same tree, and you can imagine the cacophony of a heron rookery.

We don't have great blue herons, or any kind of herons for that matter, nesting on Isle au Haut. Our summer herons are either last year's fledglings who are not yet sexually mature, or non-breeding adults. In the spring and fall, migrating adult herons forage along our shores on their way to and from their breeding grounds.

My first great birdwatching experience was with herons. I was eight years old, vacationing on Sanibel Island in Florida. While walking alone on the beach, I meandered over the low dunes flanking the shore. There was a pool surrounded by spreading trees. Herons and egrets were hunting in the pool. I crawled out on a horizontal branch over the water and lay there transfixed as the herons and egrets sparred over hunting territories and stalked for fish. A great blue heron speared a large fish right through the eyes, tossed it in the air, and swallowed it. I saw the bulge from that fish travel down the heron's long neck. The heron shook itself, readjusted its feathers, and continued stalking. I had become a birdwatcher.

Buds

In November most of our deciduous trees have shed their leaves. Only the oaks and beeches are holding on to a few stragglers. Unlike the ubiquitous spruce trees, with their conical shape and slippery needles designed to shed snow, broadleaf trees prefer to undress for the winter weather. The days are too short and cold for photosynthesis anyway. We admire the bare branches silhouetted against the sky, knowing that we won't be seeing green leaves until the spring. But amazingly, next year's leaves, and in most cases next year's flowers, are already here, on the trees, awaiting the advent of spring.

Buds form inconspicuously during the summer at the tips of twigs and in the leaf axils. The leaf axil is the angle between a leaf and the twig where it grows. While the leaves are on the trees, we don't notice the buds developing. But once the leaves fall we can see the buds for next year's growth at each twig tip and along the twig above the leaf scars where the stalks of last year's leaves let go. Because buds are formed in the axils of leaves, their placement on the stem is the same as that of leaves. On some trees, like oaks and birches, leaves and buds alternate along the stems, while on others, like maples, they are opposite each other along the stems.

A bud encloses the embryonic sprout from which a leaf or flower develops. Some buds hold only leaves, some only flowers, and some both leaves and flowers. On trees that need to survive winter weather, buds are covered by waxy scales that protect the delicate inner parts from drying out. A single bud may contain one or several rudimentary folded leaves or flowers. As the cold of winter settles in, trees go into a state called dormancy that helps them to survive harsh weather. Dormant buds are resting and cannot be awakened before they experience a prolonged period of cold. If you cut a twig from a dormant tree, bring it indoors, and put it in water, it will not leaf out unless sufficient chilling has previously occurred. This is why we can't force flowering branches until late in the winter.

Sometimes when you look at winter branches from afar, it seems they all look the same. But if you take the time to study them closely you can learn to tell trees apart by looking at their winter branches. The shapes and sizes of the buds, their placement on the stems, the number and arrangement of the bud scales, the color and texture of the buds and stems, and many other features are indicative of individual tree species.

On Isle au Haut, red oak, red maple, and paper birch are the three most common deciduous trees. Red oaks have multiple end buds—each twig end sports a cluster of pointy, many-scaled buds. The larger buds will produce the male flowers, called catkins, the smaller will open into leaves. Red oaks' female flowers are very small, and their buds, which are too small to see in the fall, appear in spring along the stems with the leaf buds, alternately along the twigs. Red maple, like oak, has multiple end buds, big and round and red, which will produce the bright, early spring bloom of these trees. The leaf buds, along with more flower buds, are opposite each other along the stem in pairs. Birch trees have delicate, pointy, alternate leaf buds along the stems. The catkin buds develop in the fall, and you can see them all winter, like little fingers at the ends of the birch twigs. Go out and look!

In the late fall, last year's leaves are beginning the process of decomposition that will turn them into soil. We still scuff a few dry leaves underfoot, and wet layers of maple and oak leaves cover the trails. The bare trees stand like skeletons of their summer selves. The world can look very gray in November. But in the season when the trees seem so lifeless and winter stretches bleakly before us, it is encouraging to know that next year's leaves and flowers are all packed up and ready for spring.

Harbor Seals
(Phoca vitulina)

Every year in late October harbor seals start hauling up on the rocky ledges between York Island and Isle au Haut. We can see them from our house. Sometimes there are 100 or more seals out there, lying in the sun. At high tide, when the ledges are under water, many seals float vertically in the water, noses up, with their chins facing the sunshine. While I'm putting my garden to bed I can hear them across the water, grunting and groaning to each other. It's good to have another big mammal around, one that won't eat my garden or my chickens.

Photo By Marnie Davis

Harbor seals live in northern temperate and arctic coastal waters around the earth, with a global population of five to six million. They vary in color from brown to tan to grey, and are dappled with lighter or darker spots, making each individual unique. Adults are five to six feet long, weigh from 220 to 300 pounds, and live up to 35 years. They have two rear flippers for propulsion and two side flippers for steering. Harbor seals can swim twelve miles per hour. Like many marine mammals, they carry a layer of blubber that helps them to maintain their body temperature in cold water. They are inquisitive creatures, and often approach boats for a close look. However, they are shy when hauled up on their favorite resting spots, and will flee when approached by boats or people. It is a violation of federal law to disturb seals or any other resting marine mammals.

Harbor seals eat fish, crabs, squid, and mollusks. Lobstermen will tell you that seals steal bait. Seals must catch ten to twenty pounds of food per day. Though they do not see well on land, their large, dark eyes are well adapted for hunting in dark or murky water. Even blind seals can hunt successfully using their highly sensitive whiskers to find food. Harbor seals tear their food off in chunks or swallow it whole, and can crush shells and crabs with their molars. They are able to dive as deep as 600 feet and stay under water for 30 minutes, though they usually hunt nearer the surface, with an average dive time of three minutes. When diving deep, seals slow their heart rate down to about five beats per minute, and channel their blood supply to their heart, lungs and brain to conserve oxygen. They exhale before a deep dive to reduce the amount of buoyant air in their lungs. Seals can store oxygen in their blood and muscles as well as in their lungs.

Harbor seals reach sexual maturity at three to six years old. New England seals come to their breeding grounds, mostly on the coast of Maine, during the summer. Females come into heat shortly after weaning their last year's pups, usually during the summer. Courtship and mating take place in the water. The fertilized egg stops developing when it is a small ball of cells and floats free in the uterus for one to three months before implanting. This gives the mother a chance to recover strength and body mass after her previous pregnancy and nursing.

Gestation takes nine to eleven months, depending on how long the implantation was delayed. Pups are born onshore in spring or early summer. Pups can swim as soon as they are born, and are very vocal with their mothers. The mother seal nurses her baby for four to six weeks with rich, fatty milk. She leaves her pup on shore while she hunts, and then returns. So if you ever find a baby seal on the beach, leave it alone. Its mother will return to it soon. Baby seals, born at about 20-25 pounds, double their weight before weaning. After weaning, they leave their mother, and join up with other young seals.

Shortly after mating, harbor seals molt and regrow their fur, and at this time need to be on land for extended periods. It stands to reason that while they are giving birth, taking care of pups, nursing, and finally molting, seals prefer remote haul-outs. They reappear on our ledges in late fall when these sensitive times are past.

Because they are top predators, seals concentrate toxins from their prey. Research done by the Marine Environmental Research Institute in Blue Hill has shown that levels of toxic chemicals in Maine harbor seals' bodies are among the highest in the world. Flame-retardants, PCB's, dioxins, various pesticides, and heavy metals all pollute our seals' tissues. That tells us that our local fish are carrying a lot of poisons that we eat too. This is a sad but common story of human interference with the health of the animals with whom we share our earth.

Winter

White-tailed Deer in Winter
(Odocoileus virginianus)

Hard times are here for white-tailed deer on Isle au Haut. The bonanza of apples that provided abundant forage in October and early November is gone. The leaves have fallen, the grass has withered, and the green plants have died away. Temperatures are falling, the winds are cold, and snow is on the way. Scarcity and hardship will be the reality for our deer in the coming months. Yet the majority will survive because of the skills and adaptations that equip them for the rigors of winter.

Photo by John DeWitt

White-tailed deer range from northern South America to southern Canada. Scientists divide the species into 38 different subspecies that vary a great deal in size and weight. The largest white-tailed deer live in the coldest part of their range, which includes Maine. Large size in a cold climate helps the deer to conserve heat in winter. The larger the animal, the lower the ratio of surface area to volume, which means that the animal radiates less heat per unit of mass, and stays warmer in a cold environment.

White-tailed deer are crepuscular animals. They are consistently active at dawn and dusk, although they can be active at any time of day. Songbirds and other diurnal animals must forage in winter during the short hours of daylight. For deer the short day length is not a serious impediment to feeding. They are adapted to low light conditions. They lack the ability to distinguish reds and oranges (thus the selection of orange as the high visibility clothing for hunters—the deer can't see it), but their eyes are extremely sensitive to light and to movement and they are able to see well even at night.

White-tailed deer shed their coat twice a year, in the spring and in the fall. Their summer coat of reddish hair has solid shafts and no undercoat. They lose this summer pelage in the fall and grow a shaggy new coat of grey-brown winter hair with hollow shafts and a dense, wooly undercoat, both of which provide excellent insulation. Just as birds can adjust the angles of their feathers to puff them out and increase their insulation value, deer have muscles that adjust the angle of their hair for maximum warmth in harsh weather.

In summer, deer eat many herbaceous and woody plants as well as mushrooms, ferns, and fruits. In the fall deer put on weight, storing body fat in preparation for the winter. They enter the cold season with about thirty percent of their body weight in stored fat. When green plants are no longer available, they eat dried grasses, nuts, and twigs. This winter diet is lower in protein and nutrients and requires more energy to digest than their summer fare. White-tailed deer are ruminants, with four-chambered stomachs. They eat intensively during their active feeding hours, then retreat to safe grounds to chew their cud at leisure. In winter the balance between the energy it takes to digest fibrous, nutrient-poor food and the energy that is gained in digesting it is almost even.

Food gets harder to find as the winter goes on, and the deer burn their stores of fat and lose weight. Research shows that does, most of whom are carrying fawns, actually delay fetal development in the first two months of gestation so that about three quarters of the energy needed to grow a fawn is consumed in the last trimester of the 200-day pregnancy, after spring green-up. If the winter is long and harsh, many deer may die from starvation, and the surviving animals may not be fit to bear healthy young in the spring.

On Isle au Haut there is a shortage of preferred food for deer in the winter. Spruce, the dominant tree, is considered by wildlife managers to be a starvation food. There is almost no understory in the spruce forest, and maples, birches, and cedars are few and far between. Most palatable tree species have been browsed as far up as the deer can reach, and seedlings are devoured, leaving a dearth of young hardwood trees. In winter our deer venture onto the ice of Long Pond and browse all the mature white cedar growing along the shore. When I swim in the summer it looks as if a topiary artist has cut a straight horizontal line about five feet from the water's surface all the way down the east side of the lake. One advantage for coastal deer in winter is that they can go into the intertidal zone at low tide and eat rockweed.

In the late fall, does and their fawns from the previous spring come together in large groups and dramatically reduce the size of their range. The bucks don't gather in groups until December when their testosterone levels drop after the fall rut. Before that, they are too aggressive to get along with other deer. All the deer eventually seek sheltered places called "deer yards" in which to avoid the bitter winds and deep snow of winter. The best deer yards are in mature spruce and spruce/fir forests where tall evergreen trees intercept much of the snowfall. Good deer yards are sheltered from the prevailing winds, taking advantage of landforms like valleys, depressions, and slopes. They also must be near winter food sources. There is no point in eating if the journey to find food takes more energy than the food provides.

Gathering in groups in winter has several advantages for deer. An established network of trails reduces the amount of energy required to move through deep snow. The deer's familiarity with these trails helps them to move efficiently to preferred foraging grounds. The herd also provides safety from predators. On the island, the only predators of deer are humans and coyotes. Deer escape predators by running away, and they must be constantly vigilant. A tracker who examines a deer yard after new snow will notice that the depressions in the snow made by resting and sleeping deer show that they all face different directions so that any approaching predator will be noticed.

As we enjoy our warm houses and prepare for the holidays it is good to remember that humans are not the only animals that find safety and comfort in gathering together in the winter. For the deer, this time of gathering is also the beginning of their period of privation. Deer must bed down in the snow. They face hunger, cold, fear, and weariness. But the mothers keep their young nearby and watch out for them, and the group provides its vigilance and security for all. Let's wish the deer well as the winter arrives in earnest.

Christmas Trees
(*Picea* spp.)

For me, it feels magical to bring a tree indoors to celebrate the holidays. On the island most people cut a spruce tree because that is what we have growing all around us. We hope to get a red spruce (which fortunately is more numerous than white spruce) since white spruce has a distinctive, unChristmassy cat-pee odor. Traditional Christmas trees are usually balsam fir, because firs do not shed their needles when they dry, and they have a lovely, wintery fragrance. No matter what kind of tree you have, fresh greenery in the living room at the darkest time of year is part of the festivity of the season.

Christmas trees are all conifers, or cone-bearing trees. The common conifers on Isle au Haut include several species of spruce and pine, balsam fir, and American larch, also known as tamarack or hackmatack. They all have needles and make their seeds in cones. The larch is not evergreen, and sheds its needles in the fall. But the rest stay green all year, with spruce dominating all other tree species, both evergreen and deciduous. Why do some trees have needles instead of broad leaves? Why do they hold onto their needles all winter? And why do they predominate on the island?

Conifers are adapted to island life in many ways. Having needles instead of leaves is useful because during the frozen wintertime trees can't get moisture from the earth or move it through their tissues. In winter water is all in the immovable form of ice. But it can turn directly from ice into water vapor—a process called sublimation. This makes drying out a big danger for winter trees. Needles, with their small surface area, waxy coating, and few pores, are designed to conserve water and avoid drying. Island soils are mostly poor, shallow, and acidic. In the absence of abundant nutrients the amount of energy it takes for a tree to regrow all its leaves every year is hard to come by. Conifers do shed their needles eventually, but only drop about 20 percent of them each year, and never have to replace their entire canopy all at once. Most of our conifers have aromatic, sticky resin, which they secrete to protect themselves from insect infestations and fungal diseases.

All of our conifers are adapted to shallow, rocky soils. Their roots spread laterally rather than deeply. When conifers shed their needles, they contribute to the acid content of the soil, perpetuating the conditions most conducive to their kind. The sheer number of needles both enhances photosynthesis and creates such deep shade that few competing plants can grow in the forest understory. The conical shape and downward sloping limbs of conifers help them in winter to shed heavy snow and avoid broken branches.

Conifers are the most ancient form of tree. They arose more than 300 million years ago, after mosses, ferns, and other primitive plants, and they soon dominated the earth's forests. Today, despite the greater diversity of flowering trees, the worlds tallest, heaviest, thickest, and oldest trees are all conifers. Conifers, which predated flowering plants by more than 150 million years, pioneered a new form of reproduction. Conifers produce male and female seed cones. Male seed cones are tiny, scaly structures that cluster among the needles in the spring. They are barely noticeable unless you look closely, but the male seed cones produce huge amounts of pollen, the plant version of sperm cells. Pollen is blown far and wide by the wind. When spruce pollen is blowing, you may find a skim coat of yellowish powder floating on ponds, piling up on the shore, and covering your windshield. Pollen grains also blow onto the female seed cones and fertilize the ovules, or egg cells, inside them. The fertilized female seed cones grow into the woody cones we all know. Each species of conifer has a unique, distinguishing variety of cone.

Before Christianity became widespread, people in many northern cultures brought evergreen branches indoors in the winter to remind them that cold and darkness would soon give way to light, warmth, and new growth. Christmas trees originated in 15th century Germany where a popular Christmas mystery play about Adam and Eve included an evergreen tree decked with apples. Christmas trees spread from churches to guild halls, and finally, in the 18th and 19th centuries, into people's homes. Puritanical America was late to adopt the Christmas tree, which did not become popular until the turn of the 19th century. I'm glad we still enjoy them today. In this dark season, when lights twinkle in Christmas trees all over the island through the long winter nights, I feel that I am joining with people from many generations before me and finding in my tree a promise of the return of light and the rebirth of spring.

Ladybugs
(Coccinellidae)

Every year in the late fall ladybugs appear in the house. I have friends who consider them pests, but for me, they are cheerful winter companions. I enjoy seeing them massed in the corner of a ceiling, crawling around on my windows, and journeying across a page of my book when I'm reading in bed. I always feel a little sad when I vacuum one up or send it down the drain by accident.

Ladybugs are members of an insect order called Coleoptera, commonly known as beetles. There are more species of beetles than of any other order of animals. Beetles are wildly successful creatures, constituting about 25 percent of all known multicellular life forms, and about 40 percent of all known insects. Aristotle named them Coleoptera, or "sheathed wing," for their characteristic hard wing covers. When flying, beetles always lift these covers in order to unfold their wings. Flying beetles have a distinctive appearance because of the way they hold their wing covers up and away from their actual wings. Ladybugs seem to have some difficulty refolding their wings at times, and you can often see an untidy wing edge protruding from under the hard, bright wing cover.

There are more than 5,000 species of ladybugs worldwide, with over 450 native to North America. Ladybugs got their English name in Britain, where the seven-spotted ladybug is the most familiar species. People called them "Lady beetles" after the Virgin Mary, also known as "Our Lady." The seven spots on the ladybug symbolized the seven joys and seven sorrows of Mary. Early British paintings of Mary often show her in a red robe with seven dark spots.

Ladybugs are considered beneficial insects because they eat aphids and other pests that suck the juices out of garden plants. A single ladybug can eat thousands of aphids, whiteflies, mealybugs, scale insects, and mites in a one- to three-year lifetime. Ladybugs' bright colors and cute appearance add to their appeal. The bright colors are actually a warning to their enemies. When disturbed, ladybugs can exude a toxic alkaloid that tastes and smells terrible, and deters hungry predators from feeding. If you bother a ladybug, you may notice that it gives off a bad smell.

The life cycle of the ladybugs is like that of butterflies, flies, bees, and many other insects. They undergo metamorphosis. Ladybugs lay eggs; the eggs hatch into tiny larvae; the larvae eat lots of aphids and shed their larval skins several times as they grow. Then they pupate. In the course of four or five days, the ladybug's body rearranges itself inside the pupa into its adult form. When this process is complete, the adult ladybug hatches out of the pupa.

Every insect species that lives in a cold climate needs to have a way to survive the winter as eggs, larvae, pupae, or adults. Ladybugs overwinter as adults. As temperatures drop in the fall, they seek big, south-facing objects such as a trees, rocks, logs, or buildings. They shelter in large numbers in deep cracks in bark, under debris, or inside house walls. They enter a state called diapause, the insect term for hibernation, becoming dormant until temperatures rise above 55 degrees. If you were to keep your house in the low 50s all winter, your ladybugs would stay asleep.

The ladybugs that enter our houses in the fall are not native American ladybugs. They are an Asian variety that was first imported in 1988 for biological control of aphids on pecan trees. Since then the Asian ladybug has spread through much of the United States and Canada, supplanting many of our native species. An interesting characteristic of the Asian ladybug is that, in contrast to native ladybug species, which have specific color patterns, different individuals of the Asian species have varying numbers of spots. Whether you love them or find them a nuisance, Asian ladybugs are here to stay. When you teach your children the old nursery rhyme, "Ladybug, ladybug, fly away home," you may actually be inviting them in.

Atlantic Sea Scallops
(Placopecten magellanicus)

Moving to an island where fishing is the basis of the economy has been an interesting journey for a naturalist like me. I have learned to consider marine animals not only as fascinating members of ecosystems, but also as resources. Halibut, cod, lobsters, crabs, shrimp, clams, mussels and scallops are species I've learned about not only from field guides and personal explorations, but also from fishermen, scientists, and regulators. I often listen to our fishermen discussing regulations and concerns about fishing resources. I read in the local papers about how scientists, regulators, and fishermen are grappling with the interests of human and animal communities, attempting to promote sustainability for both.

On the Atlantic coast as far south as North Carolina scallop fishing takes place in offshore waters year round, and is regulated by the federal government. In the Gulf of Maine, scallop fishing is seasonal and takes place within three miles of shore, mostly in small boats that fish for lobsters the rest of the year. The State of Maine regulates our scallop fishery by specifying the type of dredging gear that may be used and by restricting the length of the fishing season. In the past fifty years, Maine landings have ranged from 170 million to 320 million pounds, and 2012 was one of the best years ever. On December 2nd, Maine's 70-day 2013 scallop season began. Some of our local fishermen are now out dragging for scallops in bitter weather and stormy seas while I'm at home learning about scallops in the comfort of my warm study.

Scallops live in all the world's oceans. Their iconic shells, with radiating lines and fluted forms, are familiar to us all. Atlantic sea scallops, along with clams, mussels, and oysters, belong to a class of mollusks called bivalves. Bivalves are characterized by two hinged shells, or valves, that can open and close. The shells open to allow water to flow through, and to let the animal extend parts of its body outside the shell. They close to protect the animal from predators and, in some cases, to avert drying. The hinge has interlocking teeth that prevent the two shells from becoming misaligned. The muscles that control the valves are called adductor muscles, and, in most bivalves there are two of them. When you pick up a clam or mussel shell, you can see on the inside of the shell the scars where the adductor muscles attached. Scallops have only one large adductor muscle, which is the round white meat we love to eat. In the US, scallops are shucked on board the boat, and everything but the adductor muscle is discarded.

Scallops need their large adductor muscles because, unlike most other bivalves, they are active swimmers. They move by rapidly clapping their shells open and closed, jetting water out on both sides of the hinge and scooting forward erratically through the water. Scallops need to be able to see as they swim. Scallops have eyes—about a hundred bright blue eyes—located in tissue along the edges of both shells. Instead of having lenses, the eyes are lined with mirror-like reflectors. They are sensitive to light and darkness, and can detect movement, locate predators, and recognize areas rich in food.

Scallops are filter feeders. They eat plankton—tiny plants and animals that drift in the water. Scientists believe that scallops use their vision to move towards areas in the water where larger planktonic organisms are moving slowly, the optimum feeding condition for a scallop. Scallops do not have siphons to suck water in and squirt it out again. Instead, they swim about with their shells gaped open, allowing waterborne food to pass over internal membranes that are sticky with mucous to capture the food.

Scallops are often found in aggregations called scallop beds. In cold northern waters such as those around Isle au Haut, scallops can be found in shallow water, usually on sand or gravel bottoms. They share these areas with sponges, whelks, crabs, lobsters, sea stars, sea cucumbers, and many other creatures. Scientists are concerned about the disruption of these rich undersea habitats by scallop dredges, and are studying the question of how much permanent damage the dredges do to the ecology of the sea floor.

Sea scallops have interesting gender identities. Most scallops are either male or female, but a few are hermaphroditic. Some begin their lives as males and become females as they get older. Male sex organs are whitish when engorged with sperm, while female sex organs are bright reddish pink when engorged with eggs. A large female scallop can produce hundreds of millions of eggs annually. The sex organs, called roe, are considered a delicacy in Europe, where scallop fishermen keep the entire animal instead of just the adductor muscle for the delectation of consumers.

Scallops breed in late summer and early fall. The males in any given scallop bed release their sperm into the water simultaneously, and the females gape open their shells, letting the waterborne sperm flow over their eggs. As soon as the eggs are fertilized, the female scallop releases them into the water. The eggs sink to the bottom and hatch into larval scallops called veligers that have no shells and use flaps for swimming. These veligers grow in stages, changing over several months of drifting in the plankton into little scallops with tiny shells that sink to the bottom to grow. The largest scallop ever caught was nine inches from hinge to shell edge, but scallops average about six inches. Scallops can live up to twenty years, but do most of their growing in the first five years of life.

Scallops are probably my favorite seafood. I am grateful to the fishermen who brave winter conditions to fish for them and who know the condition of local stocks. I am grateful to the scientists who study them and who, along with fishermen, can provide regulators with the information they need to manage scallop populations for sustainable harvests. More and more in recent years, scientists and fishermen have been working together to provide regulators with local knowledge about marine resources. Fishermen have a stake in the survival of their resources, and it makes sense for all of us that fishermen and scientists both have input into local regulatory processes.

Golden-crowned Kinglets
(Regulus satrapa)

Shortly after I moved to Isle au Haut, when my partner was building his shop and the doors and windows were not yet closed in, several tiny, gray-green birds with bright yellow crowns got trapped in the building. They proved to be quite tame and easy to catch, lying calmly in my palm and allowing themselves to be examined before I released them. They felt literally light as a feather in my hand, yet I could feel the rapid beating of their tiny hearts, the intensity of their vitality. That was my introduction to golden-crowned kinglets, which I have come to believe are the most remarkable birds that live on the island year-round.

Except for hummingbirds, golden-crowned kinglets are North America's smallest songbirds. Each weighs about as much as a quarter. They are olive gray above and pale gray below with white wingbars, tiny, thin bills, and yellow/orange crowns or crests outlined in black on tops of their heads. Golden-crowned kinglets live across northern North America. In coastal Maine, they are year-round residents of coniferous forests. You will never see one at your feeder because they feed almost exclusively on insects. Kinglets are continuously active, hunting and foraging from dawn to dusk in small groups, often mixing with brown creepers, chickadees, nuthatches, and titmice. They flit to and fro, hovering acrobatically to glean their prey of moth larvae from bark and the tips of branches. And they do this all winter.

Let us stop here to consider what this means. This miniscule bird manages to survive by finding enough tiny, frozen caterpillars on spruce twigs during each short winter day to keep himself or herself warm through each long winter night. A kinglet's normal body temperature is about 106 degrees Fahrenheit. On a zero degree night, a kinglet must maintain a 106 degree differential between its body and its surroundings. It must put on enough fat each day to survive each night—there is no wiggle room. Remember that the smaller an animal is, the greater its surface area relative to its mass, and the more quickly it cools down. What are the adaptations that allow golden-crowned kinglets to accomplish this miraculous feat?

First, kinglets are extremely well insulated. Their plumage includes much higher percentage of downy feathers than flight feathers, and they can fluff themselves up to conserve heat. They even have a tiny feather that covers each of their nostrils. At night they tuck their heads and feet into their inch-thick layer of downy feathers and huddle together in small groups in sheltered places to share the warmth of their bodies. When it is extremely cold they shiver all night as they sleep to generate body heat. Even so, to explain the kinglet's survival on bitterly cold nights, researchers theorize that a kinglet must be able to lower its body temperature by as much as 10 degrees and raise it again in the morning.

Despite all this, winter mortality of kinglets is very high. How do they maintain their population year after year? Kinglets have a reproductive strategy that allows them to produce many young in the summer to offset the huge population losses they sustain in the winter. Golden-crowned kinglets begin breeding in April, before the weather has settled into warmth. The female builds a deep cup nest of spider webs, moss, lichen, and grasses hung beneath a thick tuft of spruce twigs that will shelter the nest from snow and rain and make it almost invisible from above. She further insulates the nest with feathers, tucking the quills down into the nest lining so that the feathers make an arch curtaining the top of the nest.

Most songbirds lay four or five eggs per clutch. The kinglet lays eight to eleven eggs in two layers. Since she can only incubate four eggs under her breast, the female kinglet flushes her legs and feet with extra blood, making them very warm, and sticks her hot legs down into the lower layer of eggs, thereby incubating them with her legs and feet. Incubation lasts for fifteen days. While the female is on the nest, the male actively defends the nesting territory, fiercely driving away other male kinglets, and any other species of small bird.

When the eggs hatch, the mother stays with the nestlings to keep them warm and the father feeds the entire family. As soon as the fast-growing babies have feathers and can regulate their body temperatures, the female begins to help with feeding them. When they are about eighteen days old, they have fully feathered out and are ready to leave the nest. At this point the mother leaves the whole job of feeding the young to the father. She immediately begins the construction of a second nest and soon lays another clutch of eggs. The first brood relies on their father for food until they learn to forage for themselves about two weeks later. Once the female is incubating eggs again, the male feeds her as well the young from the first brood. Talk about an involved father! Thus one pair of kinglets may raise twenty or more young in one season.

Kinglets are common birds in our forest. As they move through the trees, they constantly call to each other with a sweet "tsee, tsee" that announces their presence. They flutter and flit cheerfully, and always seem full of life and energy. They exemplify grace and gladness in the face of daunting odds, and remind us that miracles happen every day.

Harlequin Ducks
(Histrionicus histrionicus)

I remember the first time I saw harlequin ducks on Isle au Haut. It was winter, and I took a solitary hike on the Goat Trail at the south end of the island. I scrambled over icy rocks to sit on a promontory above the wild ocean near Squeaker Cove, and I noticed a small group of beautifully marked sea ducks diving in the surf, right where it was crashing into the cliffs. They were feeding. It seemed to me an incredibly dangerous enterprise. They dived into the foaming swells, then bobbed up like corks, buoyant, busy and completely unfazed by their tumultuous surroundings. Consulting my bird book, I identified the daredevil ducks as harlequins, named after Arlecchino, an acrobatic, colorfully dressed character from Italian commedia dell'arte.

Photo by Joan Handel

There are two North American populations of harlequin ducks, one on the Pacific coast and one on the Atlantic. The Atlantic population experienced a dramatic decline in numbers in the 20th century. At the present time the population is only about 2,000 individuals. Harlequin ducks are now listed as endangered in Canada and threatened in Maine. More than half of the Atlantic population winters between Swans Island and Vinalhaven, and the majority of these return every winter to the ledges on the south end of Isle au Haut.

In the springtime, mated pairs of harlequin ducks migrate north along our coast to breeding areas in eastern and central Quebec, Labrador, northern New Brunswick, Baffin Island, and Greenland. They follow cold, fast-flowing rivers and streams inland looking for nest sites. A pair may use the same area year after year. The female makes a well-hidden nest, often on an island in the stream, usually on the ground and near the water. She lays five or six eggs in her down-lined nest, and incubates them for twenty-nine days. The ducklings hatch fully feathered and ready to find their own food with the guidance of their mother. They feed by diving in the stream to catch larval insects on the rocky streambed. Once the duck families have left the nest, mother ducks often team up with other mothers to tend their broods together. The young learn to fly when they are forty-five to fifty-five days old.

The male harlequin leaves the female shortly after she begins incubating and joins other males at traditional molting areas along the coast of Labrador. The females follow the males to the same areas after the young have fledged. By then the males have dispersed and the females molt on their own. The ducks are flightless for almost a month while they lose and regrow their flight feathers. Despite a separation of several months during the summer, harlequin ducks are monogamous, and rejoin their mates on the wintering grounds.

Harlequins arrive back on Isle au Haut in the fall. Males and females come separately, returning faithfully to the same ledges year after year. Their fidelity to their wintering sites probably helps them to find their mates. They feed voraciously much of the day, and haul up on ledges to rest, usually when the tide is low. They are agile and swift in the water, able to move against strong currents, climb slippery rocks, and wedge themselves into crevices to feed in the powerful surf. They eat crustaceans, mollusks, and other small creatures, picking them from the seaweed and the rocks. Scientists who study harlequin ducks find that many show evidence of broken bones, probably from being hurled against the rocks by the waves.

Squeaker Cove is named for the mouselike squeaks of the harlequin duck, whose common name is "sea mouse." It is a wild and forbidding place to spend the winter. When I leave the safety of my warm house in January and venture out to the icy, windswept south end of the Isle au Haut to see harlequin ducks, I am amazed at the places that some creatures call home.

Life Beneath the Snow

As I look out across the expanse of February snow the world seems lifeless. But under the snow is an unseen world bustling with activity. The interface between the snow and the ground is called the subnivean zone. The word subnivean comes from Latin and means "under the snow." In the subnivean zone many small animals find shelter from bitter cold, fierce wind chill, and hungry predators.

Once snow gets to be more than six inches deep, it literally becomes a blanket. Even when ambient temperatures are below zero, the temperature at ground level hovers around 32 degrees Fahrenheit. Geothermal heat warms the bottom of the snowpack, creating small spaces where mice, voles, shrews and other animals can survive. The geothermal warmth also transforms the snow at ground level into loose granules of ice through which small creatures can easily burrow, searching for food. The subnivean zone hides an active community of small mammals who dig tunnels, make nests, and eat caches of food—and each other—all winter long.

Red squirrels spend much of the winter under the snow. They dig snow tunnels and take cover in cozy burrows near their middens, the food stashes of spruce cones they have stockpiled throughout the summer and fall. When one midden is depleted, they move on to nest near another, utilizing their summer stores to maintain their winter activity. You can often find tunnels of red squirrels at the bases of trees or see their tracks disappear into holes in the snowy woods.

The most abundant subnivean mammals are mice and voles. Voles are especially prevalent in meadows and on lawns. You can find their long, maze-like tunnels through last year's grass when the snow melts in the spring. Voles eat mostly roots and seeds. Like red squirrels, they use caches of food they have stowed away for winter use. They gnaw the bark of trees and shrubs under the snow, often girdling and killing them. They are especially fond of fruit trees, and can do extensive damage to unprotected tree trunks. Mice are primarily seed-eaters, and prefer forest habitats.

Mice, voles, and shrews, while often solitary in the summer, congregate with others of their species in winter nests made of grasses packed into subnivean pockets, huddling together for warmth. They forage sporadically, so that there is always someone home keeping the nest warm. These small rodents also have special fat reserves called "brown fat." This type of fat, located in pads over the ribs, releases stored energy as heat when the animal is threatened by cold.

Despite the protection of snow, mice and voles are vulnerable to many winter predators. On the mainland, weasels are fierce and relentless consumers of hapless rodents. Maybe we have a superabundance of voles during the summer on Isle au Haut because we don't have a population of weasels to eat them during the winter. Shrews, the tiniest subnivean mammals, are voracious carnivores. In summer, shrews eat mostly earthworms and insects, but in winter, they turn their attention to hunting voles. Weighing less than an ounce, a shrew must eat three to four times its body weight every day to survive in winter. Shrews have poisonous saliva, and can subdue the larger voles with this toxin. Above-ground predators, primarily coyotes, foxes and owls, can hear the movements of small creatures beneath the snow. They can plunge through the surface to capture them.

I love the snow for its beauty and the wintery pleasures it brings. But for some of our mammalian relations, snow cover is what makes survival possible. So when I ski through pristine snow in the silent forest or heave another heavy shovelful of snow up over that huge pile by my driveway, I sometimes stop to think about the invisible lives unfolding beneath the snow's surface.

Great Horned Owls
(Bubo virginianus)

There is no more haunting sound in the night than the mournful hooting of great horned owls. Sometimes, when I step outside after dark to close up the chicken coop or take my dog on her last walk, I hear a pair of owls calling to each other. The hoots of the females are higher than those of the males, which makes me privy to a conversation. Though owls hoot all year long, the best time to hear them is January and February when they are at the height of their breeding season.

Photo by Marnie Davis

Great horned owls are the most common large owls in the Americas. They are easier to hear than to see because they are nocturnal. Their plumage is heavily barred, ranging from grey to brown, and their large, powerful feet are covered with feathers up to their formidable talons. Their "horns" are actually prominent tufts of feathers on top of their heads. Great horned owls range from northern Canada throughout the continental United States and Mexico, and into parts of Central and South America as far south as Tierra del Fuego. Obviously, they adapt to a wide variety of habitats, but throughout their huge range they prefer open woodlands. Mated pairs stay on their breeding grounds all year. In Maine they are the largest breeding owls. Snowy owls are larger and heavier, but breed in the arctic and only occasionally irrupt into Maine during the winter. Great horned owls weigh more than three pounds and have wingspans exceeding four feet. Females are always significantly larger than males. In the wild they live about thirteen years.

Great horned owls are the earliest breeding birds in Maine. They are monogamous and court in early winter, hooting their duets late into the night and again before dawn. They do not build nests, but take over old nests of crows and hawks or use cavities in trees and snags. Each year the male chooses the nest site and attracts the female there by repeatedly flying to it and stomping on it to get her attention. By early February the female is incubating two to four eggs while the male hunts for food for both birds. The chicks hatch after about a month, and the mother continues to brood the helpless, downy young for two more weeks. Throughout this time she depends on the male to capture food for herself and her babies. The winter nights give the male long hours for hunting, which is one reason it is advantageous for owls to breed so early in the year.

Once the chicks are old enough to be left safely in the nest, both parents hunt. By the time they are six weeks old the young are venturing off the nest onto nearby branches, and soon after that they begin to fly clumsily. But they remain dependent on their parents for food until they are three months old, and often continue to pester their parents for months afterwards, screeching loudly for food. If you hear loud screeches at night, you are probably listening to young great horned owls. Young owls do not leave their parents until the next nesting season begins. At that point, they may fly far from their birthplace, ranging widely to find mates and establish new territories. This process may take a year or two.

Great horned owls are superb hunters, well adapted to capturing prey at night. Their piercing, yellow eyes with large, vertical pupils are huge relative to their heads. If we had comparable eyes, they would be the size of softballs. Owl eyes are fixed in the sockets, and the owl, with fourteen cervical vertebrae, can turn its head 270 degrees, which it must do to direct its vision. Owl retinas are richly endowed with rods, the motion-detecting cells that we have only on the periphery of our retinas. The rods allow the owl to see the slightest movement in the dimmest light.

Owl ears are asymmetrically placed on the sides of the head. This means sound reaches one ear slightly before the other, so the owl can pinpoint the origin of a sound by triangulation. Owls hear sounds ten times fainter that we can hear, allowing them to discern a mouse or vole in its tunnel under the snow. The owl's wing feathers are soft-edged, eliminating noise caused by turbulence over the wing. The owl flies silently. It loses some speed as a result, but what it loses in speed it gains in stealth. In its own silence, the owl can hear well enough to continually hone in on moving prey. It ambushes its unsuspecting meal, killing with its powerful talons.

Hunting owls may glide slowly over the ground scanning for prey, but more often they hunt from perches adjoining open areas. They prey on many species, including snowshoe hares, small mammals like mice and voles, reptiles, amphibians, and large insects. The great horned owl is the only raptor that regularly eats skunks. Owls also hunt other birds—geese, crows, and herons as well as smaller birds. If the prey is small, the owl carries it back to the perch and swallows it whole. Many hours later, it disgorges a pellet of fur and bones, which you can sometimes find on the ground under an owl roost. Dissecting an owl pellet is fascinating. You might assemble the whole skeleton of a vole. I once found the skull of a crow in a great horned owl's pellet. Crows hate owls, and often mob them noisily. One way to find an owl in the daytime is to follow the sound of an angry mob of crows. You may be rewarded with a sighting of an owl, hunched miserably in a tree while the crows dive-bomb it.

The great horned owl has few predators, though it often falls victim to the inventions of humans. An owl was electrocuted recently by a power line on Isle au Haut. Great horned owls often collide with motor vehicles. Sometimes great horned owls kill each other. Occasionally they are killed by other large raptors in territorial disputes. But for the most part, they are not prey for any other animal. Listen for them these long winter nights as they go about the business of hunting and raising their young, unconcerned with us and our human world.

Insects in Winter

People don't spend much time worrying about what happens to insects in the winter. In the summer insects are everywhere, some bothersome, some beautiful, some strange and interesting. They are the most abundant animal life forms we encounter, and their various and particular behaviors are part of our daily experience. We marvel at butterflies, repel all sorts of biting insects, battle garden pests, trap ants, and count on pollinators to fertilize vegetables, trees and flowers. Then, come cold weather, the insects almost all disappear. How do they survive the winter and then return in such profusion when the weather warms in the spring?

Most insects have four stages to their life cycles, so there are a variety of options for overwintering. Each species braves the cold in one of the four insect life stages— egg, larva, pupa, or adult. While a few insect species, most famously the monarch butterfly, migrate south to avoid the cold, the majority have adapted to survive it.

The greatest danger to insects in cold weather is freezing. If the water in their cells freezes, ice crystals pierce the cell walls, destroying living tissues. Most insects, signaled by the shortening daylight and falling temperatures of autumn, greatly reduce the amount of water in their cells and produce glycerol, a simple sugar-based alcohol that acts as an antifreeze. Once protected in this way, an insect can enter a state called diapause, or dormancy, in which it becomes completely inactive.

Generally speaking, insects in diapause are more likely to survive in an environment with minimal temperature fluctuation. In order to avoid extremes of temperature, insects retreat into crevices in tree bark, burrow into the leaf litter, crawl deep into rotting logs, or creep deep under stones. Snow cover helps to moderate temperatures for those that spend the winter close to the ground. Some insects avoid freezing by retiring below the frost line in the soil, or overwintering in streams or beneath the ice in ponds and lakes. In all these microhabitats, temperatures do not fluctuate nearly as much as they do in the open air.

Many species simply lay eggs in some protected place and then perish, counting on the eggs to bring forth the next generation. Black fly eggs remain underwater in fast flowing streams, and complete their development in the spring. Grasshoppers and crickets lay eggs in the soil. These eggs hatch in spring and begin to feed on new vegetation. Countless aphids lay their eggs in the crevices of tree bark, providing food for chickadees, nuthatches, kinglets, and other winter songbirds.

The larva is the feeding and growing stage of the insect life cycle. We are familiar with larvae as caterpillars, maggots, grubs, and underwater wrigglers such as mosquito and midge larvae. Woolly bear caterpillars can be found crawling about in the fall looking for a safe place to enter diapause for the winter. They pupate in the spring and become Isabella tiger moths. You can find beetle grubs in rotting logs all winter. The large white grubs common in our lawns and gardens burrow below the frost line until spring. They emerge as the big, reddish beetles we call June bugs.

The pupa is the insect life stage in which metamorphosis takes place. Within the pupa, which is a cocoon, chrysalis, or other covering, the larval cells rearrange themselves from the larval form into the adult. Many flies spend the winter as pupae in the soil. Some species of butterflies and moths, such as the spectacular luna and cecropia moths, overwinter in their cocoons and emerge as adults in the spring.

Some of our most familiar insects overwinter as adults. Male mosquitoes die off in the fall, but the fertilized females crawl into cracks in tree bark and emerge to lay their eggs in the first spring puddles. Honeybees remain in their hives all winter, vibrating their wings to generate enough heat to keep the hive from freezing. They use their store of honey to provide the energy required for this winter activity. Most bumblebees and wasps die in the oncoming cold, but the fertilized queens overwinter, harboring the eggs that will become the workers for a new colony in the spring. In the early spring, you often see large queen bumblebees cruising near the ground as they look for a hole or burrow in which to begin a new season's nest. The big beautiful mourning cloak butterfly, the first butterfly of spring, spends the winter deep under loose tree bark. Next spring, when you slap your first mosquito or marvel at a luna moth or hear the clumsy June bugs bashing against your newly installed screens, let it be a reminder of the versatility and resourcefulness of insect life.

Eastern Coyotes
(Canis latrans)

Part One: Origins and Arrival

My partner Albert claims to be the first person ever to see an eastern coyote on Isle au Haut. About 20 years ago, as he drove by the gravel pit on the northeast side of the island, he spotted a large, tawny canid running across the road. It was not a dog. He knew every dog living on the island. It had to be a coyote. Where had it come from? Why was it here? After that sighting there were occasional reports of lone coyotes observed on the island. Then, about ten years ago, islanders began to hear wild choruses of yips and howls at night, to find scat and tracks on the road and trails, and occasionally to see more than one coyote at a time. Clearly, a breeding population of coyotes was established on Isle au Haut.

Photo by Marnie Davis

The history of coyotes in places like Isle au Haut began before the coyotes actually arrived. The eradication of the timber wolf and the cougar from New England in the late 1800s set the stage for the arrival of the eastern coyote, because it left a niche open for a top canine predator. By the early 20th century, western coyotes were moving eastward, taking a route through the Canadian forests north of the Great Lakes. There they encountered and interbred with the eastern wolf, also known as the Algonquian wolf.

The eastern wolf, smaller and more accepting of coyotes than the timber wolf, is related to the red wolf of the American southeast, a species now almost extinct. With the infusion of eastern wolf genes, the coyotes that began colonizing northern New England in small numbers in the 1930s and 40s were larger than their western coyote ancestors. Western coyotes weigh 20 to 30 pounds while eastern coyotes weigh 30 to 50 pounds, with a more wolflike appearance. Eastern coyotes can hunt larger prey, including white-tailed deer. They form family groups that control large hunting territories.

Eastern coyotes are highly intelligent generalists, able to adapt to a variety of habitats and hunting opportunities. Since their first forays into northern New England their range has expanded dramatically. It now includes almost all of eastern North America, from populous cities and suburban areas to the deepest wilderness. As the range of eastern coyotes has increased so has their population density. New England is currently well saturated with eastern coyotes.

Each spring, when a coyote family is expecting a new litter of pups, the parents drive off most of the offspring from the previous year. They may keep one or two of last year's young around to help care for the new family. The yearlings who are driven off must disperse. When all the land adjacent to the parents' territory is controlled by other coyote families, where is a juvenile coyote to go?

A young coyote rejected by its parents in an area as densely populated by coyotes as Deer Isle might come to the shores of Stonington and look out at the array of islands in the bay. To a desperate or adventurous individual, it might seem worth a try. Coyotes are good swimmers. Swimming island to island, the longest swim between Stonington and Isle au Haut would be about a mile. After stopping on smaller islands along the way to hunt mice, voles and snowshoe hares, our intrepid young coyote would eventually arrive on Isle au Haut, a place rich in game, big enough to support a coyote family, and devoid of coyote competitors. At first only one or two lone animals made their homes on Isle au Haut, but eventually a young male and a young female must have met, formed a pair bond, and made a family. It is interesting to speculate about the long-term ecological consequences of the presence of eastern coyotes on

Isle au Haut. The consensus among locals is that our overpopulation of white-tailed deer is decreasing due to hunting by coyotes. Will this reduce the incidence of Lyme disease on the island? Will fewer deer mean enhanced diversity of wildflowers and other herbaceous and woody plants that have fallen victim to over-browsing? I have been watching the roadsides the last few years noting that there seem to be more wildflowers than when I first came to Isle au Haut.

Coyotes have almost eliminated a somewhat bothersome overpopulation of introduced wild turkeys. These birds used to eat and disperse the seeds of Japanese barberry, our most virulent invasive plant. On the downside, the coyotes have hunted the sheep off of York Island. The beautiful meadows that graced the south end of York are now growing up in spruce. And of course pet owners fear for the safety of their cats and small dogs, which are vulnerable to predation by coyotes, though as of yet no pets on Isle au Haut have disappeared.

The arrival of a new species on an island, especially the arrival of a top predator, is a big event. A fascinating aspect of island ecology is the process by which new species of plants and animals arrive and either thrive or fail in their new environment. In general, islands have lower diversity of terrestrial species than the mainland. Islands pose special challenges to newly arrived species, regardless of whether they were introduced by humans or came by random natural processes. Isle au Haut is now adjusting to the presence of coyotes. When I go outside on these early spring nights and hear the coyotes singing as they do each year during their breeding season, I am doubly thrilled—both to listen to their stirring chorus, and to wonder how they are changing my island world.

Part Two: Ecology and Behavior

Sometimes at night our dog Lily starts barking in a particularly shrill and frenzied way that means coyotes are singing in the darkness outside. I get up, go to the door, and try to make Lily quiet down so that I can listen to the chorus of wild yips and howls on the mountain and feel a primal thrill. If I let Lily out, she runs into the yard, throws her muzzle up towards the sky and howls, expressing her ancient genetic ties to her wild canid ancestors, instinctively answering their call.

Eastern coyotes, like wolves, live in family groups with a dominant breeding pair. The other family members are young from the previous year's litter who have been allowed to stay and help raise this year's pups. Each family patrols a hunting territory of six to ten or more square miles, depending on population density and prey availability. Coyotes are mostly nocturnal, though occasionally we see them in the daytime.

Coyotes eat just about anything nutritious they can hunt or forage. In the spring they take fawns, snowshoe hares, red squirrels, voles, and shrews. In summer they expand their menu to include snakes, frogs, large insects like grasshoppers, and ripening fruits and berries. In the fall they eat blueberries, huckleberries and apples. In the winter, the pack works together to bring down deer, usually the weaker and older individuals. Coyotes will also eat carrion. Coyotes deposit their scat as territorial markers in conspicuous places like trails and roads. It's easy to find. Their changing diet is obvious if you (like me) poke at the scat with a stick to see what's in it. You may find deer hair, white or brown snowshoe hare fur, masses of blueberries, or tiny vole bones.

Female coyotes come into heat only once a year in February. Hormonal cycles program males as well to mate only in February. February is the best time to hear a coyote family as they proclaim their territorial boundaries, singing in long, rising and falling howls and choruses of yips. After mating, the parents choose a den site, often a crevice in a ledge, a hollow under a rock, or a gap under a fallen tree. The expectant parents make the original cavity larger and more comfortable by digging. The litter, averaging five to seven pups, is born after nine weeks gestation, the same as for dogs and wolves.

At first the mother stays with her pups in the den while the father hunts and brings home food. Once the pups have opened their eyes and are toddling out to play and explore, the mother may leave for short periods while one of her older children watches over the babies. Coyotes are very shy and quickly relocate their den if disturbed. When the pups are about two months old, their parents start to teach them to hunt, venturing farther and farther afield as the pups grow. In late fall or early winter, the parents drive away most of the young, who must disperse and fend for themselves as the breeding season approaches again.

People sometimes ask me whether domestic dogs and coyotes interbreed. This is indeed genetically possible. However such crosses are unlikely to succeed, because a female coyote who mates with a dog will not have the help she needs to raise her litter.

Dogs have lost the instinct of wild canids to cooperate with their mates in providing for young. Since male coyotes breed only in February, a female dog would have to come into heat at that time to attract a male coyote. Coyotes are very shy of humans and in most circumstances would be reluctant to amorously approach a female dog.

Some people are alarmed by the presence of coyotes living close by. They fear that coyotes may attack pets and livestock. People often attempt to eradicate coyotes by hunting them. However, this strategy as a method of coyote population control fails, because when coyotes' stable family and territorial structures are disrupted, the females respond by bearing much larger than normal litters—up to 14 pups. Random shooting of coyotes leads to unstable populations, greater numbers of transient young animals, and more likelihood that the very problem hunters are trying to avoid will be aggravated. Stable populations of coyotes actually decrease rather than increase unwanted human/coyote interactions. Wildlife experts advise the removal only of problem animals who are known to prey on livestock.

Isle au Haut, with its twelve square miles of territory, probably supports two coyote families. Because of the difficulty of dispersing from an island, there is pressure on the parents to keep more of their young from last year's litter. It must be very hard to drive them away when there is literally no place to go but the cold ocean. That would make perhaps ten or twelve animals year round. The coyotes seem to be coming into a balance with their prey. Most islanders believe that the deer population is a bit smaller and a bit healthier. Introduced turkeys, which used to be everywhere, have become rare and reclusive. The populations of squirrels, snowshoe hares, and voles seem to be resilient in the presence of coyotes.

In late April and early May coyote pups are being born. By the end of the summer, when this spring's pups are grown and before they disperse, there may be as many as twenty coyotes roaming the island. The fall choruses of yips and howls will be loud and complex. But for now, I like to think of those fuzzy, blind little pups squeaking and squirming in their dens, nursing and sleeping and beginning to crawl about while their families look after them.

Winter Solstice

O n these short winter days I get up in the starry dark about 5:30, have breakfast, and still have time to walk my dog before sunrise. The sky is pearly on the eastern horizon as we make our way into the woods. Everything else looks dim and grey. Slowly the light above grows and the clouds go pink. Then suddenly sunlight floods into the woods sideways. The trunks of the trees light up in patches, turning gold. The winter sun rises in the southeast, angling upward on its low, arced path across the southern sky.

Photo By Kathie Fiveash

This year (2012) the solstice on Isle au Haut takes place at precisely 6:12 AM on December 21st. At that moment, the sun is simultaneously in its lowest arc and at its southernmost point in the sky, and we have our shortest day and longest night of the year. On the day of the solstice, the sun will rise at 7:06 AM and set at 3:59 PM. It will be above the horizon for 8 hours 53 minutes and below the horizon for 15 hours 7 minutes. Starting December 21st, the days will slowly get longer, and we will be heading for spring, which officially begins on March 20th at 5:02 AM, the vernal equinox.

The farther north you go, the shorter the solstice day becomes. When you get to the latitude where sunlight passes tangentially over the tilted earth, you are at the Arctic Circle. If you lived above the Arctic Circle, the day of solstice would have no sunrise or sunset—just 24 hours of twilight due to refracted light from the sun below the horizon. The farther north you travel, the longer the period without sunlight. When you get to the North Pole, there is only one sunrise and one sunset each year. The sun sets on the autumn equinox in September and rises again on the spring equinox in March, with about seven weeks of deepening twilight after the sunset, twelve weeks of darkness around the winter solstice, and seven weeks of brightening twilight before the sunrise.

The earth has seasons because it is tilted at an angle of 23.5 degrees to the plane of its orbit around the sun. As earth revolves around the sun, different latitudes face the sun's direct rays. In our winter, the northern hemisphere tilts away from the sun. On the winter solstice, the sun is shining straight down on the Tropic of Capricorn—the imaginary line 23.5 degrees south of the equator that marks the most southerly latitude where the sun can be directly overhead at noon. As the earth continues its journey around the sun, it reaches a place in its orbit where it is no longer tilted towards or away from the sun, and the sun's direct rays fall on the equator. This is the spring equinox in March, when we have equal lengths of darkness and daylight.

The earth travels on until, on the summer solstice in June, it reaches the point in its orbit where the northern hemisphere is most tilted towards the sun. The sun's rays are falling straight down on the Tropic of Cancer—the imaginary line 23.5 degrees north of the equator that marks the most northerly latitude where the sun can be directly overhead at noon—almost 1,500 miles south of Isle au Haut. This is the summer solstice, our longest day. On the last quarter of its full orbit, the earth travels to the point where it is once again directly over the equator, not tilted towards or away from the sun. This is the autumn equinox in September, when again the day and night are of equal length.

The tilt of the northern hemisphere away from the sun at this season is the cause of our winter weather. In the winter, sunlight hits northern latitudes at an oblique angle, so the light is spread over a larger area than if it were falling directly on the earth. Also, this tilted light is travelling a longer distance through the atmosphere, which dissipates its heat. The days are short and the sunlight is weak. This accounts for the cold weather of wintertime.

The solstice, when the light is weakest and the days shortest, is in December. Why then is our coldest weather in January and early February, when the days are getting longer and the sun a bit stronger? This is called seasonal lag. Simply put, more heat is being lost than is being gained for six weeks or so following the solstice. On the solstice, our environment has already been cooling off for three months. In January, we are still cooling—the weak sunshine may be strengthening, but it does not generate enough heat to match the amount of heat that is radiating into space each day. Therefore we still have net cooling. Eventually, sometime in early February, the heat gained exceeds the heat lost, and we begin to warm up.

The solstice is upon us. It is time for northern people to gather together in the ancient traditions humans have created to ward off the dangers and fears that cold and darkness bring. Candles, evergreen wreaths, feasts and festivities all help us to face the oncoming winter and to take joy in one another. While we are at it, let's also enjoy the low sunlight spilling into our south windows and our chilly woods. It is never more precious than now.

Index

Mammals

The Physical World

Plants

Reptiles

Other titles available from Penobscot Books

If you've enjoyed reading this book, check out these other island-themed books from Penobscot Books. Visit *penbaypress.me* for full descriptions of these and other books we offer.

An Island Sense of Home: Stories from Isle au Haut
by Harold S. van Doren $37.95

I Loved This Work....I have been delightfully busy
by John T. Crowell with accompanying DVD $49.95

Island Heritage: Reminiscences on Island Life
by Joyce Hunter, Linda Nelson, Caroline Rittenhouse
and Jessica Brophy $23.95

Centennial: A Century of Island Newspapers
by James M. Aldrich $24.95

Island Chronicles
by Clayton Gross $9.95

Stonington Past & Present
by the Stonington Centennial Committee $16.95

Order online at *penbaypress.me* or call 207-374-2341.

Penobscot Books
A division of Penobscot Bay Press
P.O. Box 36, 69 Main St.
Stonington ME 04681
books@pbp.me • *penobscotbaypress.com*
207-367-2200